Margaret Thornby's
guide to
tea rooms
of Britain

Fourth Edition
(2006)

Updates available:
teatalkmagazine.co.uk

WHITEHILL PUBLISHING

creating opportunities in writing

Published by:
Whitehill Publishing
Beaumont Enterprise Centre
72 Boston Road, Beaumont Leys
Leicester LE4 1HB, England
Tel: 0116 2293102   Fax: 0116 2351844
www.whitehillpublishing.org.uk

Your help is welcomed
Margaret Thornby is always on the lookout for new tea rooms for
future guides and for **tea and tea room talk** magazine. If you know
of one, or come across one on your travels that isn't featured please
write and let her know. She can be contacted care of Whitehill
Publishing at the above address, or you can email:
margaretthornby@whitehillpublishing.org.uk

ISBN 0-9525838-1-X

Cover photograph: Nick Pollard

With thanks to Wedgwood for supplying the china, "White China", for
the cover photograph. To contact Wedgwood:
Tel: (0800) 317 412   www.wedgwood.com

Printed in England

Contents

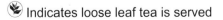 Indicates loose leaf tea is served

Introduction

Welcome to the 4th Edition of Margaret Thornby's Guide to Tea Rooms of Britain. Having spent more than fifteen years researching, visiting and writing about tea rooms, I have come to two conclusions. Firstly, tea is a drink favoured by people of all ages and those who love tea rooms and afternoon tea are men and women from every generation, from all walks of life, all cultures; the tea rooms in this Guide reflect this. Secondly, whilst technology has moved forward over the last fifteen years with the internet as a provider of a vast range of information, there is no short cut to tracking down a good tea room – it needs a personal visit. What you view on a website may sound wonderful but it has to be remembered that the internet is largely another advertising media. It also requires regular updating and can often be as out of date as an old Guide.

This Guide maintains the approach of the previous Guides – that one person (myself) has visited all the tea rooms in this book and many, many more that haven't been included. The tea rooms have been visited anonymously to ensure that I have been treated like any other paying customer and no tea room has paid in any way to be in this Guide. The selected tea rooms are my own choice; they are not graded in any way. At the time of visiting, I believe all the tea rooms in this book are worthy of inclusion.

Many people ask me which is my favourite tea room and I can honestly say that I have no favourite. Each tea room has its own unique quality and that is what I love. They are not the high street franchised chains of coffee shops that seem the same whichever town you are in. They are not the fast food outlets where speed is of the essence. What the tea rooms in this Guide share is a welcoming atmosphere where you can linger over a cup of tea, read the newspapers or meet friends. They are places where quality tea is served, often loose leaf and always in a teapot; places where food is home made and meals are freshly prepared; places where you will always find delicious and mouth-watering cakes and pastries; they are generally completely non-smoking establishments that hate mobile phones and don't smell of chips. A real tea room is always somewhere with its own unique atmosphere whether it is the music, the setting, the teapots, tablecloths, etc. Finally, it is when you put all these things together that you get that 'something extra', which makes it somewhere worth going that extra mile – whether it calls itself a tea room, a café, a coffee house, patisserie, etc.

The layout of the 4th Edition is, once again, different. I have taken heed of those stalwart readers who say that they carry the Guide with them wherever they go and have tried to make it smaller, without compromising quality. Readers tell me they appreciate the comments about access, so I have tried to keep it as clear as possible. "Full Access Facilities" means there are no steps to enter or within the tea room, and there are toilet facilities designed for disabled people. As for the details on parking, I have indicated the nearest parking available with people who may need to park close in mind. I have introduced a symbol to indicate a tea room that serves loose leaf tea and I have avoided too much information about menus as these often change seasonally, as well as to tempt us all back. If loose leaf teas are important to you, it is worth asking whether a tea room serves them as this is not always stated on the menu. Some tea rooms serve both tea bags and loose leaf tea.

If, like me, you love all things tea, you may be excited to know that I am launching a quarterly magazine called **tea and tea room talk** alongside this Guide. This will give in-depth information about tea and tea rooms, keep you up to date with events and changes at tea rooms, introduce new tea rooms as I discover them and provide fascinating articles about what goes on behind the scenes to ensure you are able to enjoy your daily pot of tea. A change for this Guide is that I have not, this time, included any hotels. These provide a very different sort of experience and atmosphere; I will be featuring any hotels that I visit serving good afternoon tea in the "Luxury Afternoon Tea" section of the new magazine. Details about subscribing to "tea" are on the inside back cover.

I remain impressed at the amazing hard work tea room owners put in to making such special tea rooms. Profit margins are not always huge and many run tea rooms alongside other businesses. As franchised coffee shops seem to take over every vacant space on the high street, I am delighted to note the number of tea rooms that have been established for many, many years, as well as the number of new ones opening.

I hope that as you use this Guide on your travels, you will greatly enjoy the tea rooms and see in them what I experienced on my visit. Over half of the tea rooms included are new for this Guide; some of these were recommended by readers of the 3rd Edition. There are also some from the previous edition that I have included again, with fully updated information. If, on your travels, you find a really good tea room that is not in this Guide, do write to me care of Whitehill Publishing – I will be sure to visit it when I am next in the area.

Margaret V. Thornby

Scotland

Scotland: Aberdeen – Victoria Restaurant

140 Union Street
Aberdeen AB10 1JD
Tel: 01224 621381

Access: upstairs
Parking on street 50m
No smoking

Set above a jeweller and gift shop, Victoria's is elegant, comfortable and spacious, offering excellent food and service in true Scottish style. From Scottish specialities to delicious cakes, there is something for all tastes.

<u>Opening times:</u> Mon-Weds + Fri/Sat 9am-5pm, Thurs 9am-6.30pm. Closed local hols & 2 weeks in February
<u>Location:</u> Above Jamieson & Carry jewellers

Scotland: Auchtermuchty – The Tannochbrae Tearoom

44 High Street
Auchtermuchty
Fife KY14 7AP
Tel: 01337 827447

Access: flat throughout
Parking outside
No smoking

You can almost hear Janet say; "Aye Dr Finlay" in this comfortable tea room that feels like sitting in her own front room. An excellent pot of loose leaf tea, a warm welcome and superb cakes round off an experience that should not to be missed.

<u>Opening times:</u> Mon + Wed-Sat 10am-5pm, Sunday 12-5pm. Closed occasional 2 weeks in year
<u>Location:</u> Brown tourist signs from A91 St Andrews Rd.

Scotland: Coldstream – Calico House

44 High Street
Coldstream
Berwickshire TD12 4AS
Tel: 01890 885870

Access: 2 steps in
Parking 10-25m
No smoking

A delightful and tasteful tea room and garden patio at the rear of a gift shop. The cakes are out of this world, with Border Tart a local speciality. A simple menu served to perfection in a restful atmosphere.

Opening times: Mon-Sat 10am-5pm incl. Bank Hols, Sun (Easter-Christmas) 11am-4pm. Closed Christmas Day and Boxing Day
Location: On main street in Coldstream

Scotland: Cupar – Café Moka

29 The Courtyard
Bonnygate
Cupar KY15 4BU
Tel: 01334 650505

Access: flat throughout
Parking: town car park
No smoking

Really good home made food, tea in a strawberry design teapot and friendly service make Café Moka a place not to pass by in its setting in a small courtyard. The cheese and poppy seed scones are delicious.

Opening times: Mon-Sat & Bank Hols 10am-4pm. Closed Christmas and New Year
Location: 400yds from Cooper Corn Exchange

Scotland: Dundee – Fisher and Donaldson

12 Whitehall Street
Dundee DD2 4AF
Tel: 01382 223488

Access: full facilities
Parking outside
No smoking

A feast of cakes, tray bakes and teatime treats lures you from the window of this long-established, traditional bakers. The tea room overlooks the shop, giving you the chance to take your time to peruse the choices.

Opening times: Mon-Sat & Bank Hols. 8am-4.45pm. Closed 25/26 December & 1/2 January
Location: Just off High Street

Scotland: Dundee – Parrot Café

91 Perth Road
Dundee DD1 4HZ
Tel: 01382 206277

Access: full facilities
Parking 10-25m
No smoking

It is certainly worth going out of the centre of Dundee to find this delightful tea room. A real comfort zone, where everything is done well from friendly service, to good food and loose leaf teas. The sandwiches on home made rye bread are well worth a try.

Opening times: Tues-Fri 10am-5pm, Sat 10am-4pm. Closed Bank Holidays
Location: From city head towards Perth. Between Art College & Sindern Shopping Area

Scotland: Edinburgh – Brodies

Ottakars
57 George Street
Edinburgh EH2 2JQ
Tel: 0131 220 2943

Access: full facilities
Parking on street 50m
No smoking

Set above Ottakars book shop, sofas and comfy window seats invite you to linger over a pot of Brodies leaf tea and a delicious, home baked cake. Tea and books – a perfect combination.

<u>Opening times:</u> Mon-Sat & Bank Hols. 9am-5pm, Sun 11am-4.30pm. Closed 25/26 Dec & 1 January
<u>Location:</u> On the 1st floor at Ottakars book shop

Scotland: Edinburgh – Café Citron

14 Marischal Place
Blackhall
Edinburgh EH4 3NF
Tel: 0131 539 7977

Access: ramp in, 1 small step to toilet
Parking on street 10m
No smoking

This is just the sort of place you would wish to have at the corner of your own street. It is small yet uncluttered, serving excellent cakes, pastries and baguettes. Somewhere to read the paper and linger.

<u>Opening times:</u> Mon-Sat 7am-5pm, Sun 8am-4pm. Closed Christmas Day, 1/2 January
<u>Location:</u> Opposite Aitken & Niven store on main street through Blackhall

Scotland: Edinburgh – Clarinda's Tea Room

69 Canongate Royal Mile
Edinburgh EH8 8BS
Tel: 0131 557 1888

Access: 2 steps in, 3
within
Parking on street 25m
No smoking

Lace tablecloths, wooden tables and chairs, walls covered in old pictures, an old, marble-topped dresser weighed down with cakes and a great pot of tea make Clarinda's a truly traditional tea room. The Lady Grey tea was most refreshing.

<u>Opening times:</u> Mon-Sat 8.30am-4.45pm, Sunday 9.30am-4.45pm. Closed 24, 25, 26 Dec + 1 January
<u>Location:</u> On Edinburgh's famous Royal Mile nr. Palace

Scotland: Edinburgh – Plaisir du Chocolat

251-253 Canongate
Edinburgh EH8 8BQ
Tel: 0131 556 9524

Access: 2 steps in and
2 to tea room
Parking on street 25m
No smoking

A superb range of loose leaf teas, patisserie and entrees in the attractive art deco setting of this stylish salon de thé. An exquisitely peaceful setting to watch the world go by or read the papers. Try the Yunnan and Darjeeling blend.

<u>Opening times:</u> Daily 10am-6pm. Closed 25 Dec-2 Jan
<u>Location:</u> On Edinburgh's famous Royal Mile

Scotland: Edinburgh – Queens Street Café

Scottish National Portrait
Gallery, 1 Queen Street
Edinburgh EH2 1JD
Tel: 0131 557 2844

Access: full facilities
Parking on street 25m
No smoking

This is a tea room much enjoyed by locals and visitors, and no wonder. It is set within two rooms housing a range of portraits. The homemade food is excellent – do try a cheese scone with mustard and paprika.

Opening times: Mon-Sat 10am-4.30pm, Sundays 12-4.30pm. Closed Christmas & Boxing Day
Location: Queen St runs East – West in the city and the Gallery is at the East end

Scotland: Edinburgh – Sir Walter Scott's Tea Room

Romane and Patterson
62 Princes Street
Edinburgh EH2 4BL
Tel: 0131 225 4966

Access: up 2 flights
with lift available
Parking within 100m
No smoking

A truly traditional Scottish tea room complete with tartan curtains and tablecloths. Good home made food is on offer, including cakes and wonderful afternoon teas - just what a good tea room is all about.

Opening times: Mon-Sat & Bank Hols 9.30am-5pm, Sun 10am-5pm. Closed for Christmas
Location: On Edinburgh's main shopping street

11

Scotland: Edinburgh – The Tea Room

158 Canongate Royal Mile
Edinburgh EH8 8DD
Tel: 07771 501679

Access: 1 step in
Parking on street 25m
No smoking

Set in two small, comfortable rooms, this tea room is
the first I have ever discovered where regular tea leaf
readings take place. Tea is served in attractive Royal
Horticultural Society china, complementing excellent
food and loose leaf tea.

Opening times: Summer daily 10am-5pm, Winter
closed on Wednesdays. Dec/Jan phone first
Location: On Edinburgh's famous Royal Mile

Scotland: Edinburgh - Valvona and Crolla Caffè Bar

19 Elm Row
Edinburgh EH7 4AA
Tel: 0131 556 6066

Access: 8 steps with
seat lift
Parking on street 10m
No smoking

Set to the rear of this famous continental food store,
this smart establishment offers an excellent pot of loose
leaf tea on its own or accompanied by quality meals,
breads and pastries. Well worth a visit.

Opening times: Mon-Sat 8am-6pm, Sundays 11am-
4pm. Closed 25/26 Dec & 1/2 January
Location: At the top of Leith Walk

Scotland: Falkland – Kind Kyttock's Kitchen

Cross Wynd
Falkland
Fife KY15 7BE
Tel: 01337 857477

Access: 9 steps to toilet
Parking outside
No smoking

Kind Kyttock's was just as I remembered it from my last visit, with high standards of service, food and teas. There are many traditional Scottish specialities to enjoy and everything, including the preserves, is made in house.

Opening times: Tues-Sun 10.30am-5.30pm. Closed 24 December to 5 January each year
Location: Left at fountain in Square to Cross Wynd

Scotland: Glasgow – Bradford's Tea Room and Restaurant

245 Sauchiehall Street
Glasgow G2 3EZ
Tel: 0141 332 5071

Access: upstairs
Parking on street 50m
No smoking

A vast range of cakes and pastries are on offer in this traditional tea room set above a bakery, which was established by the great grandfather of the current proprietor. Busy with locals and visitors alike who enjoy the food and atmosphere.

Opening times: Mon-Sat 8am-5pm. Closed Bank Hols.
Location: Opposite McLellan Galleries

Scotland: Glasgow – Miss Cranstons

33 Gordon Street   Access: upstairs
Glasgow G1 3PF   Parking on street 50m
Tel: 0141 204 1122   No smoking

Evocative of a style of Glasgow tea rooms of years gone by, with huge windows where you can peer down on the busy street below from the calm of this elegant tea room. The treacle or bran scones are delicious.

<u>Opening times:</u> Mon-Sat 8am-5pm. Closed Bank Hols.
<u>Location:</u> Corner of Mitchell Street & Gordon Street, off Buchanan Street

Scotland: Glasgow – The Willow Tea Rooms

97 Buchanan Street   Access: upstairs
Glasgow G1 3HF   Parking: on street 50m
Tel: 0141 204 5242   or main car parks
                                   No smoking

A truly elegant tea room reflecting the style of Charles Rennie MacIntosh's White Room. Service is excellent, there is a good range of loose leaf teas and the food is quite marvellous. Overall, a classic tea experience and one not to be missed. I was certainly delighted to visit this beautiful tea room again.

<u>Opening times:</u> Mon-Sat 9am-5pm, Sundays & Bank Hols. 11am-5pm, Closed Christmas & New Year's Day
<u>Location:</u> Straight across from Modern Art Gallery

Scotland: Glasgow – The Willow Tea Rooms

217 Sauchiehall Street
Glasgow G2 3EX
Tel: 0141 332 0521

Access: upstairs
Parking: on street 50m
or main car parks
No smoking

From traditional Scottish savouries to delightful afternoon teas, The Willow Tea Rooms provides an exquisite setting and it is a delight that the proprietor has rebuilt the famous Willow name. True style.

Opening times: Mon-Sat 9am-4.30pm, Sundays & Bank Hols. 11am-4.15pm (closed Sundays New Year – Easter). Closed Christmas
Location: Above Hendersons Jewellers

Scotland: Linlithgow – Findlater's Fine Foods

47 High Street
Linlithgow
Edinburgh EH49 7ED
Tel: 01506 844445

Access: full facilities
Parking on street
No smoking

Set to the rear of a delicatessen, this tea room is housed in a light, airy room with wooden tables and chairs, plus a sofa at the end. The menu is very 'deli' with a fine array of splendid cakes.

Opening times: Mon-Sat 9am-4pm, Sun 12-3pm. Closed Christmas & Boxing Day, 1/2 January
Location: Middle of High Street by pelican crossing

Scotland: Luss – The Coach House Coffee Shop

Church Road
Luss
Loch Lomond G83 8NN
Tel: 01463 860341

Access: full facilities
Parking: car park 50m
No smoking

An extremely popular place to visit with a real Scottish ambience, from tartan crockery to Scottish music and speciality Scottish food. Whether you sit outside in the summer or by the fire in the winter, there is a warm and friendly welcome all year round.

Opening times: Daily 10am-5pm, closed Christmas Day
Location: Near the village church

Scotland: Peebles – The Oven Door

24 High Street
Peebles EH45 8SF
Tel: 01721 723456

Access: flat throughout
Parking
No smoking

This bright and cheerful tea room is set within a courtyard where there is additional seating during warmer weather. Cakes and scones are available in abundance and can be contemplated from your table.

Opening times: Mon-Fri 10am-4pm, Sat 10am-4.30pm.
Open Bank Hols except 25/26 Dec & 1 January
Location: Courtyard between chip shop & jeweller

16

Wales

Wales: Boncath –
Bro Meigan Gardens and Tea Room

Boncath
Pembrokeshire SA37 0JE
Tel: 01239 841232

Access: 1 step to enter
Parking on site
No smoking

This tea room is set in a 300 year old converted barn within the picturesque gardens at Bro Meigan. The proprietor offers a warm welcome and a delightful array of cakes and scones with lashings of jam and cream.

Opening times: Easter to end of October Weds–Sun + Bank Holidays 11am-6pm
Location: On the B4332 between Eglwyswrw and Boncath, West of A478

Wales: Llandudno – Badgers Café and Tea Rooms

Unit 27 Victoria Centre
Mostyn Street
Llandudno LL30 2NG
Tel: 01492 871649

Access: full facilities
Parking within 25m
No smoking

An award winning tea room and no wonder. Though set in a modern shopping centre, Badgers is traditional in every way, including staff in black and white uniform. Loose leaf Afternoon Pelham Tea is most refreshing.

Opening times: Mon-Sat 9.30am-5pm, Sundays & Bank Hols 11am-4pm. Closed 25/26 Dec, 1Jan & Easter Sun
Location: On the main street through Llandudno

Wales: Llandudno – Coffee Culture @ Ottakars

Ottakars Bookshop
Mostyn Street
Llandudno LL30 2NG
Tel: 01492 873040

Access: full facilities
Parking within 25m
No smoking

If, like me, you have a passion for books and tea, what more could you ask than an establishment with both? Coffee Culture @ Ottakars is smart, light and relaxed; the perfect place to start your latest book.

<u>Opening times:</u> Mon-Sat 9am-5pm, Sun 10.30am-4pm, Bank Hols. 10am-5pm. Closed Christmas, Boxing, New Year's Day + Easter Sunday
<u>Location</u>: Main street of Llandudno, within bookstore

Wales: Menai Bridge – Café Aethwy

5 High Street
Menai Bridge
Anglesey LL59 5EE
Tel: 01248 717001

Access: flat throughout
Parking on street 25m
No smoking

A smart, airy tea room with a comfy sofa in the window. Croissants, pastries, cakes and savouries are all to be enjoyed in this relaxing atmosphere where there are newspapers and magazines to linger over.

<u>Opening times:</u> Mon-Fri 9am-5pm, Sat 9am-4.30pm. Closed Easter, Christmas and New Year
<u>Location:</u> Main street in Menai Bridge

19

Wales: Monmouth – The Malsters Coffee Shop

9 St Mary's Street
Monmouth NP25 3DB
Tel: 01600 712083

Access: full facilities
Parking within 50m
No smoking

This is one of those places that you would wish for in your own town; part of Wigmores Bakery, a bakery in the area for 100 years, the menu is imaginative, the food delicious and the atmosphere very relaxed.

Opening times: Mon-Sat 9.30am-5pm. Closed Sundays and Bank Holidays
Location: From High St. up cobbled street - Church St, then right to St Mary's St.

Wales: Rhosygilwen – Garden Café

The Perennial Nursery
St Davids, Haverfordwest
Pembrokeshire SA62 6DB
Tel: 01437 721954

Access: 2 steps in
Parking on site
No smoking

This unpretentious little tea room is well worth a stop. It is set within a former cow shed, which is airy and light; a pleasing atmosphere to enjoy good home made fare from savouries to bara brith and great scones.

Opening times: Daily 10.30am-5.30pm. Closed November 1st - February 28th
Location: Fishguard road from St David's, bearing left to Whitesands

Wales: Ruthin – Watergate Tea Room

65 Clywd Street
Ruthin LL15 1HN
Tel: 01824 704454

Access: 1 step within
Parking on street 50m
No smoking

The menu instructs you to "sit down, have a relaxing cuppa, spoil yourself with a 'naughty' cake and watch the world go by" in this tea room set in one of the oldest buildings in town. The Welsh Rarebit is truly marvellous and the welcome here most friendly.

<u>Opening times</u>: Tues-Sat 10am-5pm
<u>Location:</u> Opposite Ruthin Gaol (tourist attraction)

Wales: Solva – Old Printing House

20 Main Street
Solva, Haverfordwest
Pembrokeshire SA62 6UU
Tel: 01437 721603

Access: 2 steps
Parking within 50m
Smoking outside only

This tea room retains many of its original features as a printing house, where local newspapers were once printed. Not much can beat enjoying loose leaf tea with a scone straight from the oven at this splendid place. Cakes are available for a variety of dietary needs. I look forward to my next visit.

<u>Opening times</u>: Daily Spring/Summer 9am-6pm, Winter 10am-5pm. Closed November & January
<u>Location</u>: 50m from car park in main street Lower Solva

Wales: St Davids – The Sampler

17 Nun Street
St Davids, Haverfordwest
Pembrokeshire SA62 6NS
Tel: 01437 720757

Access: flat within,
toilet downstairs
Parking on street 10m
No smoking

The name of this tea room refers to the owner's interest in antique, embroidered samplers. Welsh fare is in abundance, from Solva crab to vegetable cawl to Welsh wheat and apple cake. A splendid place.

Opening times: Mon-Weds, Sat + Bank Hols 10.30am-5pm, Sun 12-5pm. Closed November & January
Location: 50m on left from Cross Square

Wales: St Florence – Bramleys Tea Room

Grandiflora Garden Centre
St Florence
Tenby
Pembrokeshire SA70 8LP
Tel: 01834 871778

Access: ramp to enter
Parking on site
No smoking

Excellent quality and value for money are to be found at this tea room, which is housed within a pine log cabin at a traditional garden nursery. They specialise in healthy food from locally sourced produce.

Opening times: Daily 10am-5pm (Feb-Oct), Winter 10am-4pm. Closed 2 weeks at Christmas
Location: 3 miles outside Tenby

Wales: Trefin – Oriel-y-Felin Gallery and Tearoom

15 Ffordd-y-Felin
Trefin, Nr St Davids
Pembrokeshire SA62 5AX
Tel: 01348 837500

Access: full facilities
Parking outside
No smoking

This charming gallery and tea room proves art and tea to be a great marriage. There is a menu of loose leaf teas and excellent food made from fresh local produce, which is quite beautifully presented. I thoroughly enjoyed the Queen's Jubilee tea.

Opening times: Tues-Sun 11am-5pm, incl. Bank Hols.
Closed 1 November - Easter
Location: Trefin is off A487, in centre of village

23

West Country

Bath
Cornwall
Devon
Dorset
Somerset
Wiltshire

24

Bath – Sally Lunn's House

4 North Parade Passage 🌿
Bath BA1 1NX
Tel: 01225 461634

Access: 1 step in
Parking 50m
No smoking

Set in the oldest house in Bath, the speciality here is the famous sweet or savoury Sally Lunn buns, which are quite delicious and very satisfying. Great care is taken to ensure your visit is enjoyable – a real delight.

Opening times: Mon-Sat 10am-10pm, Sundays 11am-10pm. Closed Christmas and Boxing Day
Location: Follow street signs to Sally Lunn's House

Cornwall: Helston – The Fountain Garden Conservatory

Trevarno Estate & Gardens
Trevarno Manor, Helston
Cornwall TR13 0RU
Tel: 01326 574274

Access: full facilities
Parking on site
No smoking

This tea room has an idyllic setting overlooking the lawns of this beautiful estate and gardens. Teas and food are taken within the conservatory, where a large fountain is the centrepiece. Restful and quite delightful.

Opening times: Daily 10.30am-4.30pm (check first in Winter). Closed Christmas and Boxing Day.
Location: Penzance road from Helston, follow brown tourist signs

Cornwall: Launceston – Mad Hatter's Tea Shop

28 Church Street
Launceston
Cornwall PL15 8AR
Tel: 01566 777188

Access: several tables
on flat
Parking 100m
No smoking

Though this tea room changed hands in 2004, it has kept to its Alice in Wonderland theme of being a fun and welcoming place with character teapots. The menu is imaginative for children and adults alike - try the indecisive cake taster with a pot of Lady Grey tea.

Opening times: Mon-Sat 9.30am-5pm
Location: 100m from church, between church & square

Cornwall: Morwenstow – Rectory Farm Tearooms

Crosstown
Morwenstow, Nr Bude
Cornwall EX23 9SR
Tel: 01288 331251

Access: full facilities
Parking on site
No smoking

This tea room is set in a 13th century building where stone floors, beams, a huge fireplace, traditional tables and settles create a proper farmhouse atmosphere. You can enjoy marvellous food and loose leaf teas, just a short walk from spectacular coastal scenery.

Opening times: Daily 11am-5.30pm. Closed End Oct-week before Easter
Location: Off A39 follow signs for tea room and church

Cornwall: Poundstock –
Bangors Organic Tea Room

Bangors House
Poundstock, Bude
Cornwall EX23 0DP
Tel: 01288 361297

Access: veranda flat
1 step to house
Parking on site
No smoking

Expect spectacular views in this peaceful setting where you can savour excellent organic food and drinks in the garden, veranda or elegant tea room. Certified as an organic tea room by the Soil Association in May 2003.

Opening times: Easter (incl. all Easter weekend) -end Oct. Tues-Fri 12-6pm
Location: Just off A39 south of Bude

Cornwall: Tintagel – Lewis's

Bossiney Road
Tintagel
North Cornwall PL34 0AH
Tel: 01840 770427

Access: 6 steps within
Parking: car park 50m
Smoking in garden
only

The epitome of an English tea room with beautiful white appliqué tablecloths at tables set with white bone china. Add to this a most tempting array of cakes, leaf teas, set afternoon teas and you are in tea room heaven.

Opening times: Mon, Tues, Thurs-Sun 10am-5.30pm. Open Bank Hols. Closed 4 Jan-15 March
Location: Opposite the Chapel

Devon: Fremington Quay – The Quay Café

Fremington Quay
Bickington, Barnstaple
Devon EX31 2NH
Tel: 01271 378783

Access: full facilities
Parking on site
No smoking

In a superb setting overlooking the harbour, this spacious tea room chronicles the history of Fremington Quay with pictures and displays. It is simple and welcoming with good food including fabulous scones.

Opening times: Daily 9.30am-5.30pm. Closed Christmas & New Years Day, Mondays in Winter
Location: Single track road signed off B3233 between Barnstaple & Instow

Devon: Ilfracombe – Café Cocoa

Walker's Chocolate Emporium
6 High Street
Ilfracombe
Devon EX34 9DF

Access: upstairs
Parking on street 25m
No smoking
Tel: 01271 867193

Spotting loose leaf tea on the menu, I went upstairs to find a delightfully light and airy tea room with sofas and armchairs at one end and a spectacular sea view at the other. Chocolate features highly on the menu as you might expect, with books on chocolate to browse.

Opening times: Mon-Sat 9am-4.45pm, incl. Bank Hols.
Location: On the main street through Ilfracombe

28

Devon: Moretonhampstead –
The Gateway Tea Room

17 The Square
Moretonhampstead
Devon TQ13 8NF
Tel: 01647 440722

Access: 1 step in,
toilet upstairs
Parking on street 20m
No smoking

There is a friendly welcome at this small tea room
where food is home-made and locally sourced. Cream
teas are popular and the scones superb. A traditional
tea room in which to relax and be unhurried.

Opening times: Mon, Tues & Fri-Sun 10am-5pm.
Closed 25/26 & 31 December & 1 January
Location: Middle of village – part of National Park

Devon: Sidmouth – Fields Coffee Shop

Fields of Sidmouth
2-6 Market Place
Sidmouth, Devon EX14 8AR
Tel: 01395 515124

Access: full facilities
(ramp to tea room)
Parking within 50m
No smoking

"Service as it used to be", is the motto here and you will
not be disappointed. A friendly welcome awaits from
staff who show you to your seats and provide excellent
service and food. A real delight.

Opening times: Mon-Sat 10am-2pm & 2.45-4.45pm.
Closed Bank Hols except Good Friday, closed 6/7 Feb.
Location: Close to beach. In Fields Department Store

Devon: South Molton – The Corn Dolly

115a East Street
South Molton
Devon EX36 3DB
Tel: 01769 574294

Access: 2 steps in,
1 within tea room
Parking on street 15m
No smoking

It was quite simply a pleasure to return to this award winning 'proper tea shop', which is set within a 17th Century building, to enjoy loose leaf teas and excellent food where "nothing is too much trouble".

<u>Opening times:</u> Mon-Sat 9.30am-5pm (Weds 8.30am-5pm) Sun/Bank Hols 11am-5pm. Closed 25 Dec-2 Jan
<u>Location:</u> On main road near petrol station

Devon: Tiverton – Four and Twenty Blackbirds

43 Gold Street
Tiverton
Devon EX16 6QB
Tel: 01884 257055

Access: 5 steps in,
toilet upstairs
Parking across road
No smoking

Four and Twenty Blackbirds has olde worlde charm, with loose leaf tea and two trolleys heaving with delicious home made cakes. A visitor commented; "It was wonderful to get proper tea". I heartily agree.

<u>Opening times:</u> Mon-Sat 9.30am-5.30am, Bank Hols (incl Sundays on BH w/ends) 10.30am-4.30pm. Closed Christmas, Boxing & New Years Day
<u>Location:</u> By bridge in area known as The Pound

Devon: Topsham – Georgian Tea Room

Broadway House
35 High Street, Topsham
Devon EX3 0ED
Tel: 01392 873465

Access: 3 steps in
Parking on street 25m/
Holman Way car park
No smoking

With a strong emphasis on locally produced food and a recent change to serving loose leaf teas, this tea room is even better since my last visit three years ago. Try one of the "world famous scones". Awarded Best Tea Room in Devon for 2005.

Opening times: Tues-Sat 9am-4.45pm. Closed Sundays, Mondays, Bank Hols.
Location: Left of mini roundabout as you enter town

Devon: Totnes – Greys Dining Room

96 High Street, Totnes
Devon TQ9 5SN
Tel: 01803 866369

Access: 1 step in
Parking on street 50m
No smoking

Expect a real treat in this tea room nestled at the top of the High Street. Housed in a 300 year old building it was once, aptly, a tea merchant. The teas are of excellent quality and the food exquisite. Look out for the splendid cake cabinet – it is quite beautiful.

Opening times: Mon, Tues, Thurs, Sat 10am-5pm, Friday 9.30am-5pm. Closed Weds, Sun, Bank Hols.
Location: Top of High Street opposite Post Office

Dorset: Blandford Forum –
Cavalcade of Costume Tea Room

Lime Tree House
The Plocks
Blandford Forum
Dorset DT11 7AA
Tel: 01258 453006

Access: 1 step in,
toilet with rails/raised
seat
Parking on street 50m
No Smoking

I found this tea room to be as charming as I remembered it from my first visit in 2001. There is a simple menu of teatime treats, including cream teas.

Opening times: Easter-end Sept 10am-5pm, Oct-Easter 10am-4pm. Closed Tues/Weds and December
Location: From Market Place, off Salisbury road

Dorset: Chideock – Bay Tree Tea Garden

Bay Tree House
Duck Street, Chideock
Dorset DT6 6JW
Tel: 01297 489336

Access: 2 to terrace
Parking on site
No smoking

Though on a busy road, once you enter by the garden gate you are transported to a world of peace and tranquillity. Sitting under the large covered pergola enjoy the specialities, such as Dorset cream teas.

Opening times: Tues-Sun + Bank Hols. 10.30am-5pm. Closed November-March incl.
Location: On A25 between Bridport & Charmouth

32

Dorset: Christchurch –
New Forest Perfumery Gift Shop and Tearooms

11 Castle Street
Christchurch
Dorset BH23 1DP
Tel: 01202 482893

Access: 1 step within
Parking within 50m
No smoking

It was a first to discover a tea room set to the rear of a perfumery. There is an imaginative list of sandwiches and a trolley bearing sumptuous cakes, such as Dorset apple cake. Hand made ice creams are a speciality.

Opening times: Mon-Sat 10am-5pm, Sun 11am-5pm. Closed Christmas, Boxing, New Years Day
Location: Next bowling green/remains Norman Castle

Dorset: Dorchester – The Old Tea House

44 High West Street
Dorchester
Dorset DT1 1UT
Tel: 01305 203719

Access: flat throughout
Parking: approx 50m
No smoking

The Old Tea House was built in 1635 and has been a tea room since 1901. Today you are assured a friendly welcome and a range of excellent traditional fare.

Opening times: June-Nov Tues-Sun + Bank Hols. 10am-4.30pm, Nov-May Weds-Sun 10am-4pm. Closed January
Location: Distinctive b&w building, top of High St.

33

Dorset: Lyme Regis –
Country Stocks Georgian Tea Rooms

53 Broad Street
Lyme Regis
Dorset DT7 3QF
01297 442961

Access: flat in & within
Parking 50-100m
No smoking

I first visited this tea room on Millennium Eve and it was
a delight to visit again to find the same good service,
loose leaf teas and excellent food.   There is a range of
set teas and some quite delicious cakes.

Opening times: Mon-Sat 10am-5pm, Sun 11am-4pm,
may vary with seasons. Closed Christmas Day
Location: Centre of Broad Street, close sea front

Somerset: Dulverton – Lewis's Tea Rooms

13 High Street
Dulverton
Somerset TA22 9HB
Tel: 01398 323850

Access: flat in, 1 step
to toilet
Parking outside
No smoking

One peek through the window and you will be drawn
into this delightful tea room. Your only dilemma may be
what to choose from the menu, which includes a range
of loose leaf teas and set afternoon teas.

Opening times: Daily 10am-5pm. Closed Christmas
Day, Boxing Day & all of January
Location: Between fish and chip shop & delicatessen

Somerset: Porlock – Whortleberry Tearoom

High Street
Porlock
Somerset TA24 8PY
Tel: 01643 862337

Access: full facilities
Parking: car park 25m
Smoking in garden
only

A friendly welcome awaits at this tea room where you can relax and watch the world go by over tea and good home-made food. The Whortleberry jam is splendid.

Opening times: Tues-Sun 10am-5pm, Bank Hols. 11am-4pm. Closed 2 weeks from Christmas Eve, 2 weeks March & 2 weeks November
Location: Opposite Methodist Church

Wiltshire: Bradford-on-Avon –
The Bridge Tea Rooms

24a Bridge Street
Bradford-on-Avon
Wiltshire BA15 1BY
Tel: 01225 865537

Access: 2 steps in,
accessible toilet opp.
Parking: opposite
No smoking

Housed in a 17th century building with staff wearing Victorian dress, The Bridge is the epitome of an English tea room. Excellent service, delicious cakes and home made fare complete the experience.

Opening times: All year Weds-Sat 10am-5pm, Sundays 12-5.30pm, Mondays on Bank Hols.
Location: In town, right by Town Bridge House

Southern

Berkshire
Buckinghamshire
Hampshire
Oxfordshire

36

Berkshire: Windsor –
The Crooked House of Windsor Café Tea Room

51 High Street
Windsor
Berkshire SL4 1LR
Tel: 01753 857534

Access: 1 step in, 1
room this floor
Parking 25-50m
No smoking

Next to the Castle itself, this could be the most photographed building in Windsor. Do call in for tea, which is a real treat whether you are simply having a pot of tea or one of the splendid set teas.

Opening times: Daily 9.30am-6pm. Closed Christmas Day, Boxing Day and Easter Day
Location: Close to Windsor Castle, next to Guildhall

Buckinghamshire: Beaconsfield –
The Old Tea House

7 Windsor End
Beaconsfield
Buckinghamshire HP9 2JJ
Tel: 01494 676273

Access: flat in, 2 steps
to toilet, with grabrail
Parking on street 10m
No smoking

This tea room has been in every edition of this Guide and continues to maintain good service and serve excellent home made food, including fabulous cakes.

Opening times: Mon 10.30am-4pm, Tues-Sat 9am-5pm. Closed Bank Hols, 2 weeks Christmas/New Year
Location: Opposite St Mary's Church and village green

Buckinghamshire: Marlow – Burgers of Marlow

The Causeway
Marlow
Buckinghamshire SL7 1NF
Tel: 01628 483389

Access: lower room
flat, 3 steps to toilet
Parking 25-50m

Burgers is a long-established family business, with the tea room set to the rear of the shop that sell breads, confisserie and chocolates, all made in the craft bakery. An unhurried place in a beautiful position near to the river where daily newspapers are available.

Opening times: Mon-Sat 8.30am-5.15pm. Closed Bank Holidays
Location: Near the bridge and the church

Hampshire: Romsey – Cobweb Tea Room

49 The Hundred
Romsey
Hampshire SO51 8GE
Tel: 01794 516430

Access: 2 steps in with
grab rail, 4 within
Parking 50-100m
No smoking

A traditional tea room with beamed ceilings, round cloth-covered tables and service provided by friendly and helpful staff. An interesting cake stand bears a superb range of cakes such as delicious lemon drizzle.

Opening times: Tues-Sat 10am-5.30pm. Closed 2 weeks over Christmas and New Year
Location: On the main street – south side of Romsey

Hampshire: Selbourne – Gilbert White's Tea Parlour

Gilbert White's House	Access: full facilities
The Wakes, High Street	Parking opposite/15m
Selbourne	No smoking
Hampshire GU34 3JH	Tel: 01420 511275

I am most grateful to the reader who recommended this exquisitely peaceful and restful tea room. Sitting in this setting, listening to classical music and enjoying fare based on 18th century recipes, such as the 'Toasted Wig', was quite simply delightful.

<u>Opening times:</u> Tues-Sun 11am-4.30pm. Closed between Christmas & New Year
<u>Location:</u> Opposite church, on B3006 from Alton

Hampshire: Stockbridge – Lillies of Stockbridge

High Street	Access: flat in & within
Stockbridge	Parking within 25m
Hampshire SO20 6HF	No smoking
Tel: 01264 810754	

A tastefully decorated tea room with built-in seating where there are set times for morning or afternoon tea. Crumpets, teacakes and delicious pastries can be enjoyed along with a range of specialty loose leaf teas.

<u>Opening times:</u> 9am-4.45pm daily. Closed Christmas, Boxing, New Years Day (Jan-Mar. last orders 3.45pm)
<u>Location:</u> Centre of Stockbridge next to duck pond

Oxfordshire: Bladon –
Park House Tea Room and Antiques

26 Park Street
Bladon
Oxfordshire OX20 1RW
Tel: 01993 813888

Access: flat throughout
Parking on site
No smoking

A beautiful setting for tea where you are surrounded by antique furniture, china and pictures, which are all on sale. All the food is fresh and home made, there are lovely set teas, and cakes displayed on the sideboard.

Opening times: Daily 10am-6pm (5pm in Winter).
Closed Christmas Day
Location: Opposite St Martin's Church

Oxfordshire: Burford – The Copper Kettle

121 High Street
Burford
Oxfordshire OX18 4RG
Tel: 01993 822942

Access: 1 low ridge in,
otherwise full facilities
Parking 50-100m
No smoking

A tea room set in a building that is over 500 years old, with excellent home made food, including a splendid variety of cakes. These are on view on the large trolley stand and are certain to make your mouth water.

Opening times: Mon-Fri 9.30am-6pm, Sat, Sun & Bank Hols 10am-6pm. Closed Christmas & Boxing Day
Location: On main street, almost opposite shoe shop

Oxfordshire: Southcombe –
The Antiques Centre Tea Room

Quiet Woman Antiques Centre
Southcombe, Chipping Norton
Oxfordshire OX7 5QH
Tel: 01608 646262

Access: 3 steps in
Parking on site
No smoking

The tables here are set with attractive Victorian embroidered and appliqué cloths, teacups, saucers and plates. The proprietors have created a calm, relaxing atmosphere in which to enjoy the delicious fare.

<u>Opening times:</u> Mon-Sat 10am-4.30pm, Sun 11am-4pm
<u>Location:</u> On Chipping Norton to Oxford road

Oxfordshire: Woodstock –
Hampers Food & Wine Company

31/33 Oxford Street
Woodstock
Oxfordshire OX20 1TH
Tel: 01993 811535

Access: 1 step to toilet
Parking on street 25m
No smoking

Set to the side of a delicatessen, Hampers is a popular place for family and friends to meet and relax. The menu here is based on what is served in the deli; interesting sandwiches, baguettes and divine cakes.

<u>Opening times:</u> Mon-Sat 9am-5pm, Sun & Bank Hols. 10am-4pm. Closed 25/26 December & 1 January
<u>Location:</u> On A44 Oxford – Stratford road

41

Oxfordshire: Woodstock – Harriet's Tea Rooms

20 High Street
Woodstock
Oxfordshire OX20 1TF
Tel: 01993 811231

Access: flat throughout
Parking on street 25m
Smoking in the garden
only

A traditional tea room where delicious cream teas and
savouries are served by helpful staff. There is a great
choice of cakes and pastries; you can also take one or
two home from the cake shop of which Harriet's is part.

<u>Opening times:</u> Mon-Fri 8.30am-5pm, Sat 8.30am-
5.30pm, Sun 10am-5.30pm. Closed 25/26 December
<u>Location:</u> Middle of High Street in Woodstock

South East

East Sussex
Kent
Surrey
West Sussex

43

East Sussex: Alfriston – The Singing Kettle

6 Waterloo Square
Alfriston
East Sussex BN26 5UD
Tel: 01323 870723

Access: 1 step in
Parking on street 25m
No smoking

The Singing Kettle is housed within a 15th century smugglers cottage. It looks out over the medieval high street of Alfriston and provides a welcome, friendly place for tea. A truly traditional tea room with wonderful, freshly prepared home made food.

Opening times: Daily 10am-5pm. Closed for a few days in January
Location: In the main square

East Sussex: Brighton – The Gallery Café

Brighton Museum & Art Gallery
Royal Pavilion Gardens
Brighton
East Sussex BN1 1EE

Access: full facilities
Parking on street 50m
No smoking
Tel: 01273 292814

As its name suggests, the Gallery Café has a splendid setting overlooking one of the galleries. It is simply a fabulous place to relax, enjoy excellent service, fare and teas. A real find and one I hope to return to soon.

Opening times: Tues-Sat 10am-4.30pm, Sun 2-4.30pm. Open Bank Hols. Closed Christmas & New Year
Location: By the Royal Pavilion

East Sussex: Brighton – Mock Turtle Tea Shop

4 Pool Valley
Brighton
East Sussex BN1 1NJ
Tel: 01273 327380

Access: 1 steps in, a
few to lower floor
Parking on street 50m
No smoking

A feast of cakes (including Vegan) await you at this friendly tea room, to be enjoyed with one of the range of loose leaf teas on offer. The Mock Turtle is well known, having been open as a tea room since 1972. A marvellous sanctuary from the busy streets of Brighton.

Opening times: Daily 9.30am-6.30pm. Closed Christmas & Boxing Day
Location: Next to Pool Valley Coach Station

East Sussex: Eastbourne – Pavilion Tea Room

Royal Parade
Eastbourne
East Sussex BN22 7AQ
Tel: 01323 410374

Access: flat throughout
Parking approx 25m
No smoking

Whether you visit on a bitterly cold January morning or a warm July afternoon, Pavilion Tea Room is a welcome place, serving loose leaf teas and delicious fare to visitors and locals alike. A spectacular setting.

Opening times: Daily 10am-5pm (Winter 10.30am-4.30pm). Check for times at Christmas
Location: Close to Redoubt Fortress on seafront

45

East Sussex: Hove – The Tea Rooms

Hove Museum & Art Gallery
19 New Church Road
Hove
East Sussex BN3 4AB
Tel: 01273 292837

Access: full facilities
Parking: on site (with badge) or on street
No smoking

It is unusual to find a 'proper' tea room within a museum but this one more than satisfied my criteria. Excellent home made cakes and savouries, a good pot of tea and a calm ambience – just superb.

Opening times: Tues-Sat 10am-4.30pm, Sun 2-4.30pm. Closed on Bank Holidays
Location: Follow tourist signs for museum

East Sussex: Lewes – Robson's of Lewes

22a High Street
Lewes
East Sussex BN7 2LN
Tel: 01273 480654

Access: 1 step within
Parking outside
No smoking

A popular, friendly tea room overlooking an attractive courtyard garden. A place to enjoy good home made fare over the newspapers or conversation with friends. A welcome rest from the bustle of the busy town.

Opening times: Mon-Fri 9am-4.30pm, Sat 9am-5pm, Sun & Bank Hols.10am-6pm
Location: Half way up High St

East Sussex: Rye – Cobbles Tea Rooms

Cobble Cottage, Hylands Yard
Rye
East Sussex TN31 7ED
Tel: 01797 224347

Access: flat throughout
Parking on street 25m
Smoking in garden
only

Don't miss this quite superb tea room tucked away along a cobbled yard. A warm welcome awaits, along with a choice of loose leaf teas – including Russian Caravan which is one of my favourites – and some excellent fare on which to feast.

<u>Opening times:</u> Daily 10am-5pm. Closed 24-27 Dec
<u>Location:</u> Just off High Street opposite The Bell

East Sussex: Rye – Cranberries

105a High Street
Rye
East Sussex TN31 7JE
Tel: 01797 224800

Access: 2 steps to
2nd level
Parking on street 25m
No smoking

It is hard to walk by this pretty tea room without being tempted in by the fantastic array of wonderful home made cakes in the window display. Inside, you will not be disappointed; the cakes taste as good as they look and there is a warm and friendly welcome.

<u>Opening times:</u> Daily 10.30am-5pm. Closed Weds in Winter. Phone to check Christmas times
<u>Location:</u> On main shopping street in Rye

East Sussex: Winchelsea – The Tea Tree

12 High Street
Winchelsea
East Sussex TN36 4EA
Tel: 01797 226102

Access: flat in, 3 steps
to garden + 2 to toilet
Parking outside
No smoking

It was a pleasure to return to this charming tea room
and to find the quality of fare, teas and service was as
excellent as I remembered from my last visit. Most
definitely a place to seek out and enjoy.

Opening times: Mon (except Nov-March), Weds-Sat
10am-5pm, Sun 12-5pm. Closed Christmas/New
Years Day & January
Location: Centre of town between Town Gate & church

Kent: Penshurst – Fir Tree House Tea Rooms

Fir Tree House
Penshurst
Kent TN11 8DB
Tel: 01892 870382

Access: full facilities
Parking outside
Smoking: garden only

Although there is a menu of set teas, you are welcome
to 'mix and match' to create your own ideal choice.
The home made cakes are truly delicious and loose
leaf tea makes the perfect accompaniment.

Opening times: Tues-Sun & Bank Holidays 2.30-6pm.
Closed November-March
Location: Centre of village, next to village hall

Kent: Penshurst –
Quaintways 16th Century Tea Room

High Street Access: 2 steps in
Penshurst   Parking outside/15m
Kent TN11 8BT   No smoking
Tel: 01892 870272

Quaintways is set within 16th century cottages that were
once the bakehouse - the Victorian oven is still in place
in the tea room. There is a daily choice of superb
cakes and savouries to enjoy; all made by one of the
proprietors using local produce.

<u>Opening times:</u> Tues-Sun & Bank Holiday Mondays
10am-5pm. Closed week before Xmas, re-opens Feb.
<u>Location:</u> Centre of village, at T-Junction

Surrey: Richmond - The Original Maids of Honour

288 Kew Road, Richmond   Access: flat throughout
Surrey TW9 3DU   Parking on street 50m
Tel: 0208 940 2752   No smoking

The Original Maids of Honour has an incredibly long
history of serving teas and its famous cake, from which
it takes it name. Decorated in traditional tea room
style, this busy place should not be missed.

<u>Opening times:</u> Tues-Sat 9.30am-5.30pm. Closed
Bank Hols
<u>Location:</u> Opposite Kew Gardens

49

West Sussex: Chichester – Shepherd's Tea Room

35 Little London
Chichester
West Sussex
Tel: 01243 774761

Access: 1 step in,
toilet upstairs
Parking opposite
No smoking

Attention to detail is a priority at this tea room - food is beautifully presented and the taste superb, there is a good range of loose leaf teas and the atmosphere is unhurried. Certainly a place not to be missed.

Opening times: Mon-Sat 9.15am-5pm, Sun & Bank Hols 10am-4pm. Closed 25/26 Dec, Easter Sunday
Location: Near Suffolk House Hotel & Museum

West Sussex: Chichester – St Martin's Organic Tea Room

3 St Martin's Street
Chichester
West Sussex PO19 1NP
Tel: 01243 786715

Access: 1 step in,
toilet upstairs
Parking: car parks
No smoking

This tea room takes great pride in serving excellent, organic fare, with menu choices to satisfy a variety of dietary needs. There are many quiet corners in which to savour the experience in this historic setting.

Opening times: Mon-Fri 10am-6pm, Sat 9am-6pm. Closed some Bank Holidays
Location: Off East Street

West Sussex: Henfield –
Norton House Olde English Teahouse

The High Street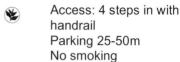
Henfield
West Sussex BN5 9DB
Tel: 01273 492064

Access: 4 steps in with
handrail
Parking 25-50m
No smoking

I was thrilled to discover that this traditional tea room
was still serving loose leaf tea, wonderful cakes and
savouries after over 36 years in business – quite an
achievement and certainly well worth visiting.

Opening times: Fri, Sat & Mon 9.30am-5pm, Sun &
Bank Hols 10am-12noon & 3-5pm.
Location: Centre of Henfield

West Sussex: South Ferring – The Pantry

1a The Pantiles
Ferringham Lane, S. Ferring
West Sussex BN12 5NE
Tel: 01903 503957

Access: flat throughout
toilet with 1 grabrail
Parking outside/50m
No smoking

This small tea room, a mobile phone free zone, offers a
warm welcome and good home made fare. It is
frequented by locals as well as visitors from far afield
who enjoy the delicious cream teas.

Opening times: Mon & Tues, Thurs-Sat 9am-5pm.
Closed Bank Holidays + occasional weeks March/Oct
Location: 1st of 3 shops on Ferringham Lane

London

London: SE1 – Bramah Tea and Coffee Museum

40 Southwark Street
Bankside
London SE1 1UN
Tel: 0207 403 5650

Access: flat throughout
Nearest tube: London
Bridge
No smoking

This is definitely a tea connoisseur's paradise with a wide range of loose leaf teas served in the tea room, as well as sold in the shop. Enjoy afternoon tea to the sound of live piano music. An absolutely must visit, with a fascinating museum of tea and coffee on site.

Opening times: Daily 10am-6pm. Closed Christmas Day and Boxing Day
Location: Nearest tube/railway station London Bridge

London: SW1 – Ladurée Parisian Tearoom

Harrods
87-135 Brompton Road
London SW1X 7XL
Tel: 0203 1550111

Access: full facilities
Nearest tube:
Knightsbridge
No smoking

Close to the famous Harrods Food Hall, Ladurée provides a welcome rest from your shopping, and an excellent setting for afternoon tea, lunch or tea and cakes. With comfortable chairs, excellent tea and fare, it is hard not to linger to savour the experience.

Opening times: Mon-Sat 9am-9pm, Sundays 12-6pm
Location: On the ground floor at Harrods

London: SW1X – Patisserie Valerie

17 Motcomb Street Access: 2 steps in
London SW1X 8LB   Nearest tube:
Tel: 0207 245 6161   Knightsbridge
                              No smoking

This wonderful Patisserie provides the feel of a perfect Sunday morning place to relax, read the paper, meet up with friends … The food is quite splendid, with a positively mouth-watering display of cakes and patisserie, with options for different dietary needs.

<u>Opening times:</u> Mon-Sat 8am-6pm, Sundays 9am-6pm. Closed Bank Holidays
<u>Location:</u> Next to Carlton Tower Hotel

London: SW1X – Urban Retreat Café

Harrods   Access: full facilities
87-135 Brompton Road   Nearest tube:
London SW1X 7XL   Knightsbridge
Tel: 0207 730 1234   No smoking

Urban Retreat Café provides a splendid setting for tea, overlooking the famous Harrods Egyptian Escalators. The speciality here is healthy food using organic ingredients. Harrods is a vast store, giving the 'excuse' for several tea breaks – be sure not to miss this one.

<u>Opening times:</u> Mon-Sat 10am-7pm, Sun 12-6pm
<u>Location:</u> 5th Floor at Harrods next Egyptian Escalators

London: SW3 – Baker and Spice

47 Denyer Street
Chelsea
London SW3 2LX
Tel: 0207 589 4734

Access: flat throughout
Nearest tube: Sloane
Square
No smoking

Here you feel as though you can create an impromptu family, as you sit at the large, shared table, which has huge slabs of butter and milk jugs ready for use. From savouries to pastries the food is divine, with an emphasis on organics.

Opening times: Mon-Sat 7am-7pm, Sat & Sun 8.30am-5pm. Closed Christmas and New Year
Location: Back of Walton Street

London: W1 – Art Bar Café

Liberty
Regent Street
London W1
Tel: 0207 573 9555

Access: full facilities
Nearest tube: Oxford
Circus
No smoking

The Art Café Bar is set within Liberty's very ornate building and is a comfortable, relaxed setting for tea with classical music adding to the atmosphere. Delightful full afternoon tea is available from 3-5.30pm.

Opening times: Mon-Sat 10am-6.30pm (7.30pm Thurs) incl. Bank Hols, Sun 12-6.30pm. Closed 25/26 Dec.
Location: On the 2nd floor at Liberty

London: W1 – Patisserie Valerie

162 Piccadilly Access: 3 steps in
London W1J 9EF   Nearest tube Green Pk
Tel: 0207 491 1717   No smoking

This central London tea room provides a delightful
setting to enjoy excellent food, service and teas. The
traditional Croque Monsieur is simply delicious. A
relaxing place where you can discover the history of
'Valerie' on the menu.

Opening times: Mon-Fri 7.30am-8pm, Sat 8am-8pm,
Sun 8am-7pm. Open Bank Hols. Closed 24/25 Dec.
Location: Opposite Royal Academy of Arts

London: W1 – Saint James' Lounge

Fortnum and Mason Access: full facilities
181 Piccadilly   Nearest tube: Green
London W1A 1ER   Park/Piccadilly Circus
Tel: 0207 734 8040   No smoking

I tried Sri Lankan Lover's Leap tea in this beautiful
lounge with elegant turquoise china. There is a large
tea menu which has tea blends and rare teas.
Afternoon teas are luxurious, with excellent service,
comfort and style the hallmark of Fortnum and Mason.

Opening times: Mon-Sat 10am-5.30pm (Afternoon Tea
3-5pm, Lunch Tues-Sat 12-2pm)
Location: On the 4th Floor at Fortnum & Mason

London: W1 – Yauatcha

15 Broadwick Street
London W1F 0DL
Tel: 0207 494 8888

Access: full facilities
Nearest tube:
Tottenham Court Rd
No smoking

Youatcha is unlike any other tea experience, serving blue, black, white, green and even ancient teas in oriental teapots and bowls. Expect the unusual and enjoy watching staff perform the tea ceremony.

Opening times: Daily 11am-11.45pm
Location: corner of Berwick & Broadwick Street

London: W8 – Kandy Tea Room

4 Holland Street
London W8 4TL
Tel: 0207 937 3001

Access: 1 room flat, 1
& toilet downstairs
Nearest tube: High St.
Kensington
No smoking

This is a charming and elegant tea room, where superb loose leaf teas from the various regions of Sri Lanka are served from exquisite bone china teapots. The afternoon tea is fabulous – this is a place not to miss.

Opening times: Wed-Fri 12-5pm, Sat & Sun 12-6pm.
Closed 2nd week July-end Aug, 2 weeks Christmas
Location: Just off Kensington High Street

London: WC2E – Paul

29-30 Bedford Street
Covent Garden
London WC2E 9ED
Tel: 0207 836 5321

Access: 1 step in
Nearest tube: Covent Garden
No smoking

Set in stylish Covent Garden, Paul fits in perfectly. From breakfast through to afternoon tea, you can expect food of exceptional quality and taste. There is a wide range of wonderful breads and exquisite patisserie, and comfortable, relaxed surroundings.

Opening times: Mon-Fri 7.30am-9pm, Sat & Sun 9am-9pm
Location: Near Henrietta Street

Heart of England

Gloucestershire
Herefordshire
Shropshire
Staffordshire
Warwickshire
West Midlands
Worcestershire

Gloucestershire: Brockweir –
The Village Shop and Café

Mill Hill, Brockweir
Gloucestershire GL15 6UQ
Tel: 01291 689995

Access: full facilities
Parking on site
No smoking

Part of a project established by local residents and housed within a building that is environmentally friendly, this lovely tea room has a simple menu and uses wonderful crockery – worth seeking out.

Opening times: Mon-Sat 8.30am-5pm, Sun & Bank Hols. 10am-3.45pm. Closed Christmas Day
Location: Near Tintern

Gloucestershire: Cheltenham –
Frère Jacques Patisserie and Café

11 Montpellier Arcade
Cheltenham
Gloucestershire GL50 1SU
Tel: 01242 250402

Access: 1 room
& toilet downstairs
Parking on street 50m
Smoking in arcade

Set in an arcade with smart shops, Frère Jacques fits in well. Choose from the delicious array of pastries and cakes available in this smart and delightful tea room.

Opening times: Mon-Sat 8.30am-5.30pm, Sun & Bank Hols. 10.30am-4.30pm. Closed 25/26 December
Location: Opposite the Queen's Hotel on the main road through Cheltenham

Gloucestershire: Cheltenham – Thatchers

101 Montpellier Street
Cheltenham
Gloucestershire GL50 1RS
Tel: 01242 584150

Access: 1 in, 12 to toilet
Parking opposite
No smoking

From breakfast through to afternoon tea, expect good service and excellent home made food in this relaxed tea room. A great place to escape busy Cheltenham and enjoy a traditional tea room experience.

Opening times: Mon 10am-2pm, Tues-Sat + Bank Hols. 9am-5pm, Sun 12-4pm. Closed 25/26 December
Location: From Queen's Hotel into St Georges Road, then 1st left – 50m on left

Gloucestershire: Tetbury – Tetbury Gallery Coffee Room

18 Market Place
Tetbury
Gloucestershire GL8 8JG
Tel: 01666 503412

Access: 1 step in
Parking on street 20m
No smoking

Tea is served in silver teapots, a feast of cakes beckons from the sideboard and the menu offers a choice of savouries which are quite beautifully presented. All together a wonderful experience.

Opening times: Daily - please phone to check
Location: In the Market Place in Tetbury

61

Gloucestershire: Tetbury – Two Toads Tea Room

19 Church Street
Tetbury
Gloucestershire GL8 8JG
Tel: 01666 503 696

Access: flat throughout
Parking approx 50m
No smoking

I was so pleased to return to this tea room and find the quality of fare and service remained so high. Looking around, people were relaxed over newspapers and pots of loose leaf tea – simply taking life at a slow pace. This is a superb tea room with a separate tea menu.

Opening times: Mon-Sat 9am-5pm, Sun & Bank Hols. 10.30am-4.30pm. Closed Christmas/New Year's Day
Location: Near the Market Square

Herefordshire: Hereford – Antique Tea Shop

5a St Peters Street
Hereford HR1 2LA
Tel: 01432 342172

Access: flat throughout
Parking 25-50m
No smoking

I adore the tablecloths at this tea shop, which are hand embroidered on crisp, white linen. The simple menu has quality food and cakes to be enjoyed with one of the loose leaf teas on offer – well worth a visit and a peaceful place away from the bustle of busy Hereford.

Opening times: Please telephone the tea room to check their opening times
Location: Off Union Street

62

Herefordshire: Ledbury – Mrs Muffins' Tea Shop

1 Church Lane
Ledbury
Herefordshire HR8 1DL
Tel: 01531 633579

Access: 1 step in, 1 to
lower room & toilets
Parking within 50m
No smoking

Housed in a 17th century building on a cobbled street,
Mrs Muffins offers excellent Herefordshire fare and is a
truly traditional tea room. It was certainly a pleasure to
return and enjoy the calm, relaxed atmosphere. There
is an excellent variety of cakes – all home made.

Opening times: Daily 10am-5pm. (Sun. Mar-Oct only)
Location: Behind the Market House in lane to church

Herefordshire: Leominster – Emporium Tea Shop

Drapers Lane
Leominster
Herefordshire HR6 8ND
Tel: 01568 615064

Access: 2 steps in
Parking: Square – 50m
No smoking

This tea shop has a friendly welcome and an emporium
of cakes on which to feast your eyes – it will be hard to
make a choice and even harder to resist. Lady Grey
tea in delicate cups completes the experience in this
580 year old building that was once a chocolate shop.

Opening times: Mon & Tues, Thurs-Sat 9.30am-4pm.
Closed Bank Hols, Christmas – New Year
Location: Drapers Lane runs down from the Square

63

Herefordshire: Monkland – Monkland Cheese Dairy

The Pleck
Monkland, Leominster
Herefordshire HR6 9DB
Tel: 01568 720307

Access: 1 low step in,
spacious toilet
Parking on site
No smoking

This charming tea room, set at Monkland Cheese Dairy, is one I was delighted to return to. I do enjoy a tea room with a theme and the fabulous cheeses are prominent here and also available to buy to take home.

Opening times: Daily 10am-5.30pm. Closed Christmas Eve – 9 January & Sundays Christmas-Easter
Location: Tourist signs on A44 West of Leominster

Herefordshire: Pembridge – Marston Meats Farm Shop and Tea Room

Marston Court
Pembridge, Leominster
Herefordshire HR6 9JA
Tel: 01544 388328

Access: full facilities
Parking on site
Smoking in garden
only

This tea room located in an old, oak-beamed stable in idyllic Herefordshire countryside is well worth seeking out. There is loose leaf tea, home made cakes, cream teas and lunches using the meats from the farm shop.

Opening times: Easter – Christmas Weds-Sun 10am-6pm. Closed Bank Holidays
Location: A44 Pembridge to Kington, follow 'pig' signs

Herefordshire: Ross on Wye – Antique Tea Shop

40 High Street
Ross on Wye
Herefordshire HR9 5HD
Tel: 01989 566123

Access: 1 step in
Parking 25-50m
No s~

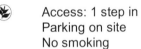

This charming tea ~ ~ ~irs, linen
and lace tablecloth ~ s was
one I was delighte~ ~he
atmosphere relaxed ~ ~e.

*Now Pots and Pieces
See updates on
teatalkmagazine.co.uk*

<u>Opening times:</u> Mon- ~ 9.45am-5pm, Sun 10.15am-
5pm. Closed Mon, Tues, Weds Nov-Easter, 25/26 Dec
<u>Location:</u> Near striking 17th C Market Hall

Herefordshire: Walford –
Walford Court Garden Café and Tea Room

Walford, Leintwardine
Herefordshire SY7 OJT
Tel: 01547 540570

Access: 1 step in
Parking on site
No smoking

Whether you sit in the attractive garden or within the
tea room, you can be sure of a friendly welcome and
excellent home made, vegetarian fare. Muffins are a
speciality and quite delicious.

<u>Opening times:</u> Summer daily 10.30am-4.30pm, Winter
to 3pm. Closed occasionally – phone if travelling
<u>Location:</u> At Walton take Lingen & Presteigne road,
then left – follow Walford Court sign

65

Shropshire: Church Stretton –
Berry's Coffee House

17 High Street
Church Stretton
Shropshire SY6 6BU
Tel: 01694 724452

Access: 1 step within
Parking outside
Smoking outside only

With a commitment to using local producers, fair trade and organics food, this award winning tea room has a number of rooms, plus courtyard. From a piece of toast to one of many cakes, everything is of excellent quality.

Opening times: Weds 11.30am-5pm, Thurs-Sat 10am-5pm. Closed Christmas and Boxing Day
Location: Off The Square in middle of Church Stretton

Shropshire: Clungunford –
Bird on the Rock Tearoom

Abcott, Clungunford
Shropshire SY7 0PX
Tel: 01588 660631

Access: flat throughout
Par⌐ n site
⌐g

Now Rocke Cottage
Tearooms
See updates on
teatalkmagazine.co.uk

An award winning te⌐ ⌐me,
excellent stand⌐ ⌐ome
made food. I ar⌐ ⌐ea room;
the scones are st⌐

Opening times: We⌐ ⌐ank Hols 10.30-5.30pm
(5pm in Winter). Clo⌐ _ days after bank Hols
Location: On B4367 to Clungunford follow tourist signs

66

Shropshire: Hilton - The Old House Tea Lawns

The Old House
Hilton, Bridgnorth
Shropshire WV15 5PJ
Tel: 01746 716560

Access: Gardens flat,
1 to tea room
Parking outside
No smoking

I happened upon this tea room during my travels and was enchanted by the beautiful gardens where you can find a quiet spot under gazebos or parasols to enjoy one of the set teas. All the food is home made at this wonderful tea room that is well worth a visit.

Opening times: May-end Oct. Weds-Sun & Bank Hols 12-5pm
Location: On A454 from Bridgnorth - signed

Shropshire: Ludlow – De Greys

5 Broad Street
Ludlow
Shropshire SY8 1NG
Tel: 01584 872764

Access: 1 step in
accessible toilet
Parking on street 25m
Smoking to rear only

An extremely popular tea room set to the rear of a bakery. You may have to wait a while but it will be worth it to enjoy quality fare in this traditional tea room.

Opening times: Mon-Thurs 9am-5pm, incl. Bank Hols. Fri & Sat 9am-5.30pm, Sun 11am-5pm. Closed Christmas Day & New Years Day
Location: Just below Buttercross Clock Tower

Staffordshire: Codsall – Flappers

The Square, 1 Church Road
Codsall
Staffordshire WV8 1EA
Tel: 01902 845562

Access: 1 low step in
Parking within 25m
No smoking

Tea is served in bone china tea sets which arrive on trays with lace mats. There is an excellent range of scones and the 'mix and match' crumpets, muffins and toasties with fillings of your choice are quite splendid.

Opening times: Mon-Sat 8.30am-5pm. Closed Bank Hols. & Christmas Eve – day after New Year
Location: In triangle with 2 pubs: The Crown & The Bull

Staffordshire: Leek –
Greystones 17th Century Tea Room

23 Stockwell Street
Leek
Staffordshire ST13 6DH
Tel: 01538 398522

Access: 5 steps in
Parking: car park 25m
No smoking

A friendly welcome awaits at Greystones, which is so popular you may have to wait a short while to be seated. I am sure you will find it well worth it when you sample the positively splendid home cooking.

Opening times: Weds & Fri 10am-3pm, Sat 10am-5pm generally all year with occasional closure for holidays
Location: Macclesfield to Buxton road near car park

Warwickshire: Dunnington – The Garden Café

Hillers, Dunnington
Heath Farm, Alcester
Warwickshire B49 5PD
Tel: 01789 491950

Access: full facilities
Parking on site
No smoking

This tea room was even better than I remembered it and busy even at 10am. There is a daily choice of specials, some excellent home made cakes and a generally relaxed atmosphere in which to enjoy it all.

Opening times: Daily 9am-5pm. Closed Christmas & New Year's Day
Location: On the road south of Ragley Hall

Warwickshire: Shipston-on-Stour – Mrs Brown's Tea Room

23a High Street
Shipston-on-Stour
Warwickshire CV36 4AJ
Tel: 01608 662217

Access: low ridge in, flat throughout
Parking on street 15m
No smoking

A traditional tea room setting, with wonderful home made traditional cakes and cream teas characterises the delightful Mrs Brown's. It is popular with locals and visitors alike, and provides a welcome place to stop.

Opening times: Mon-Sat 9.30am-4.45pm. Closed Bank Holidays
Location: To rear of Lloyds TSB Bank in Square

Warwickshire: Warwick - Brethren's Kitchen

The Lord Leycester Hospital
60 High Street
Warwick CV34 4BH
Tel: 07776 257604

Access: full facilities
Parking on site
No smoking

Housed in a beautiful, historic building with wood panelling and a vast fireplace, this is the perfect setting for traditional afternoon tea. You will not be disappointed by the marvellous home made cakes and savouries on offer.

Opening times: From end March Tues-Sat 10am-5pm, Sun 11am-5pm. Open Bank Holiday Mondays
Location: Left off Westgate to Brook St to car park

West Midlands: Birmingham – Hudson's Coffee House

122-124 Colmore Row
Birmingham B3 3AU
Tel: 0121 236 9009

Access: 2 steps in
Parking on street 25m
No smoking

In this large and busy city, full of coffee bars and fast food places, Hudson's is a quiet haven and claims to be the only privately run coffee house in the city. Beautifully presented gourmet sandwiches are a speciality – quite delicious. One to return to.

Opening times: Mon-Sat 10am-5pm. Closed Bank Hols
Location: Near Victoria Square

West Midlands: Birmingham – Hudson's Coffee House

Birmingham Midland Institute
Margaret Street
Birmingham B3 3BS
Tel: 0121 2361233

Access: upstairs
Parking on street 10m
No smoking

A delightful setting in a long, narrow room with quotes about tea painted on the walls. Take a newspaper or magazine, order your favourite loose leaf tea and simply enjoy the opportunity to relax – a great place.

Opening times: Mon-Sat 10am-3pm. Closed Bank Hols and Christmas week
Location: Close to Birmingham Museum & Art Gallery

Worcestershire: Broadway – Tisanes Tea Rooms

Cotswold House
21 The Green, Broadway
Worcestershire B50 4AW
Tel: 01386 853296

Access: 2 steps in,
ramp available
Parking: car park near
No smoking

Some tea rooms seem to just get everything right, and Tisanes is one of them. The service is swift, efficient and friendly, the choice of loose leaf teas extensive, and the food on offer quite superb. A 'must visit'.

Opening times: Mon-Sun & Bank Hols 10am-5pm. Closed Christmas Day
Location: In centre of village

Worcestershire: Chaddesley Corbett - Chaddesley Corbett Tea Room

The Post Office
Chaddesley Corbett
Worcestershire DY10 4SA
Tel: 01562 777257

Access: 2 steps in with grabrails
Parking outside
No smoking

This is an impressive little tea room where things are done 'properly' from loose leaf tea, to bone china tea sets, to embroidered linen tablecloths, to tea forks with which to eat delicious home made cakes. I urge you to seek it out on your travels.

Opening times: Mon-Sat 10am-4pm. Closed Bank Hols
Location: Signposted from A448

Worcestershire: Pershore – The Abbey Tea Room

31 Broad Street
Pershore
Worcestershire WR10 1BB
Tel: 01386 550367

Access: 1 step in,
toilet upstairs
Parking outside
No smoking

This spacious, airy tea room offers food and loose leaf teas of an excellent quality. I enjoyed a perfectly made pot of Darjeeling, which was quite marvellous in taste, and savoured the restful atmosphere – just splendid. Due to launch their own label loose leaf tea shortly.

Opening times: Mon-Sat 9.30am-6pm, incl. Bank Hols.
Location: 300m from Abbey

East Anglia

Cambridgeshire
Essex
Hertfordshire
Norfolk
Suffolk

Cambridgeshire: Cambridge – Aunties Tea Shop

1 St Mary's Passage
Cambridge CB2 3PQ
Tel: 01223 315641

Access: 1 step in, toilet
downstairs
Parking: within 100m
No smoking

Aunties Tea Shop has provided tea, savouries and cakes to visitors since 1979 and maintains the atmosphere of a traditional tea room. Service is swift and friendly and all cakes are made on the premises.

Opening times: Mon-Sat 9.30am-6pm, Sun & Bank Hols 10.30am-5.30pm. Closed 25/26 Dec & 1 January
Location: Opposite St Mary's Church

Cambridgeshire: Ely – Peacock's Tearoom

65 Waterside
Ely
Cambridgeshire CB7 4AU
Tel: 01353 661100

Access: full facilities
Parking outside
Smoking in garden
only

A truly wonderful tea room serving over 50 varieties of loose leaf tea in a welcoming and relaxing atmosphere. Afternoon tea has finger sandwiches, scones and cakes on beautiful silver stands – quite marvellous. Sit inside or in the pretty front garden by the wisteria.

Opening times: Weds-Sun & Bank Hols 10.30am-4.30pm. Closed approx 1 month from New Year
Location: Follow signs for The Maltings, close to river

74

Cambridgeshire: Grantchester – The Orchard

Mill Way
Grantchester
Cambridgeshire CB3 9ND
Tel: 01223 845788

Access: flat throughout
Parking on site
No smoking

A visit to this area simply wouldn't be complete without stopping for tea at The Orchard, where there is a long history of serving teas to many famous writers. It is a truly memorable experience to sit in the orchard tea garden on a fine day.

<u>Opening times:</u> Summer daily 9am-7pm, Winter daily 9am-5.30pm. Closed for Christmas
<u>Location:</u> On Mill way just below the church

Cambridgeshire: Kimbolton – Buttercups

15 High Street
Kimbolton, Huntingdon
Cambridgeshire PE28 0HB
Tel: 01480 861000

Access: 1 step in
Parking outside
No smoking

Buttercups is busy with locals, as well as visitors to this attractive village. There are armchairs and sofas in which to relax and indulge in tasty sandwiches, or one of the many wonderful cakes also on sale in the bakery.

<u>Opening times:</u> Mon-Fri 8.30am-5pm, Sat 8.30am-4pm. Closed Bank Holidays
<u>Location:</u> On the main shopping street in the village

75

Cambridgeshire: St Ives – River Tea Room

Bridge Street
St Ives
Cambridgeshire PE27 5EG
Tel: 01480 464921

Access: flat throughout
Parking opposite -
Dolphin Hotel
No smoking

A very popular tea room, once the Manor House, serving excellent home made fare from its pretty riverside setting. Service is efficient and friendly, the atmosphere relaxed. A delightful place to stop for tea.

Opening times: Mon-Fri 10am-4pm, Sat 10am-5pm, Sun 11am-4pm, Bank Hols 10am-4 (or 5) pm
Location: Next to the historic bridge on the river

Essex: Danbury – Tea on the Green

3 Eves Corner
Danbury
Essex CM3 4QF
Tel: 01245 226616

Access: low ridge in,
then flat, incl. toilets
Parking outside
No smoking

I loved sitting in this tea room overlooking the village green. A delightful menu from breakfast through to afternoon tea. Children and adults alike cannot resist gazing at the cake table to make their choice.

Opening times: Mon-Fri 8.30am-4.30pm, Sat & Sun 10am-5pm, Winter Mon-Fri 8.30am-4pm, Sat 10am-4pm, Sun 11am-4pm. Closed Christmas week
Location: Opposite duck pond on village green

Essex: Dedham – The Essex Rose

Royal Square, High Street
Dedham
Essex CO7 6DE
Tel: 01206 323101

Access: flat in, 1 step
to accessible toilets
Parking within 10-25m
No smoking

A traditional tea room set within three rooms of a 16th century building that was once an ironmonger. Cream teas, luxurious gateaux and an indulgence of cakes to choose from and enjoy with your tea.

Opening times: Summer daily 10am-5.30pm, Winter daily 10am-4.30pm. Closed 25-28 Dec inclusive
Location: Village centre opposite church

Essex: Finchingfield – Causeway Tea Cottage

2 The Causeway
Finchingfield
Essex CM7 4JU
Tel: 01371 810431

Access: 2 steps in,
1 within
Parking on street 25m
Smoking: garden only

A quintessentially English village and tea room, which overlooks the village green and pond. It is hard not to be drawn to the wonderful cakes on view which taste as good as they look. It is well worth seeking out this delightful tea room – I thoroughly enjoyed going back.

Opening times: Summer Mon-Weds, Sat & Sun 10am-6pm, close at 5pm in Winter. Closed occasionally
Location: From Great Dunmow B1057 to Finchingfield

Essex: Great Dunmow – The Tea Tree

15a North Street
Great Dunmow
Essex CM6 1AZ

Access: flat throughout
Parking: some outside
No smoking

This tea room sells duck food but don't worry this is for you to feed to the many ducks in the pond which The Tea Tree overlooks. Modern in style but with traditional touches, good service and great food. A lovely and restful setting for tea.

Opening hours: Mon & Tues, Thurs-Sat 10am-5pm, Sun & Bank Hols 11am-4pm
Location: On B184 next to Doctor's Pond

Essex: Heybridge Basin – The Lock Tea Room

Basin Road
Heybridge Basin, Maldon
Essex CM9 4RS
Tel: 01621 854466

Access: 1 step in, accessible toilet
Parking within 50m
No smoking

In an idyllic setting overlooking the river, you can sit outside on the decking or inside in the light, spacious tea room to enjoy tea and excellent food in this calm atmosphere. Owned by Wilkin and Son, so try one of the Tiptree jams. Certainly a place to linger.

Opening times: Daily 9am-5pm incl. Bank Hols. Check opening times during Winter months
Location: Just off B1026

Essex: Thaxted – Cake Table Tearoom

4/5 Fishmarket Street
Thaxted
Essex CM6 2PG
Tel: 01371 831206

Access: 1 step in
Parking on street 10m
No smoking

The Cake Table has a splendid tea menu, listing over twenty loose leaf teas. I can never resist Kwazulu tea as a perfect accompaniment to a home made scone. A fine, traditional tea room in a historic village.

Opening hours: Mon & Tues 10.30am-4pm (Winter until 3pm), Weds & Fri, Sat (& Sun on Bank Hol. w/ends) 10.30am-4.30pm. Closed Thursdays
Location: To the rear of the Guild Hall

Essex: Tiptree – The Tea Room

Wilkin & Son Ltd
Tiptree
Essex CO5 0RF
Tel: 01621 814524

Access: full facilities
Parking on site
No smoking

Based at the headquarters for Tiptree jam, there is also a shop selling their wide range of jams, chutneys and sauces. These can be enjoyed in the busy tea room, which attracts many visitors and is well worth a visit.

Opening times: Mon-Sat & Bank Hols. 10am-5pm, 11am-5pm Sundays. Check for Winter opening times
Location: B1023 in Tiptree

Hertfordshire: Berkhamsted – The Attic Café

Home and Colonial 🌿
134 High Street, Berkhamsted
Hertfordshire HP4 3AT
Tel: 01442 878713

Access: up 3 flights of
stairs
Parking on street 25m
No smoking

If you can manage the three flights of stairs, where you
can always stop to browse the antiques, there is a real
treat in store. Sample the splendid home made fare,
including delicious cakes and pastries, with a pot of tea.

Opening times: Mon & Tues, Thurs-Sat 10am-5pm,
Sun & Bank Hols 11am-4pm. Closed 2 weeks Xmas
Location: on the main street in Berkhamsted

Hertfordshire: Kings Langley –
Agapanthus Antiques and Tea Room

38 High Street 🌿
Kings Langley
Hertfordshire WD4 9HT
Tel: 01923 268786

Access: 1 step in
Parking within 25m
No smoking

Loose leaf tea is served in antique teapots and can be
accompanied by one of the marvellous cakes. A
friendly welcome and the chance to contemplate a
purchase of one of the unusual and tasteful gifts.

Opening times: Mon-Sat 9am-5pm, Sun 10am-4pm
(Easter-Sept). Closed Bank Hols & Xmas-New Year
Location: On the main street in Kings Langley

Hertfordshire: Radlett – The Bull Pen Tearooms

Battlers Green Farm
Common Lane
Radlett
Hertfordshire WD7 8PH

Access: full facilities
Parking on site
No smoking
Tel: 01923 857505

Situated in what was once a bull pen, you can expect attention to detail from good service and excellent food, to loose leaf tea and co-ordinated crockery. A splendid tea room and certainly worth seeking out.

Opening times: Tues-Fri 9.30am-5pm. Sat & Sun 9am-5pm. Closed over Christmas & New Year
Location: Signposted from A41

Hertfordshire: West Mill –
West Mill Tea Room and Bistro

West Mill Village Green
West Mill, Buntingford
Hertfordshire SG9 9LG
Tel: 01763 274236

Access: flat throughout
Parking outside
No smoking

There is little to beat enjoying tea and scones whilst looking out over a classic village green. Whether sitting inside on cool days or out in the sun, the smell of home baking from the kitchen is quite wonderful.

Opening times: Tues-Thurs 9.30am-5pm, Fri to 7pm; Sat, Sun & Bank Hols 10am-7pm. Closed Christmas
Location: Off A10

Norfolk: Aylsham – The Old Tea Rooms

18a Red Lion Street
Aylsham
Norfolk NR11 6ER
Tel: 07733 377852

Access: 1 step in
Parking 50m
Smoking in garden
only

This friendly tea room has two rooms plus a garden in which to enjoy tea and excellent fare. Specialising in traditional recipes and home baking, you may get jam tarts if there is pastry to spare!

<u>Opening times:</u> Mon & Tues, Thurs & Fri 10am-4pm, Weds & Sat 10am-3pm. Winter closing 1 hour earlier. Closed Bank Hols & Christmas week
<u>Location:</u> Close to Aylsham Market Place

Norfolk: Cley next the Sea – West Cottage Café

New Road
Cley next the Sea
Norfolk NR25 7RA
Tel: 01263 740891

Access: steps to both
garden and tea room
Parking: 3 opposite
No smoking

Just as you think you have found all of this tea garden, another section emerges, revealing many quiet spots to enjoy tea and wonderful cakes. I recommend the home made tea cakes, which were absolutely fantastic.

<u>Opening times:</u> Daily 10.30am-5pm (unless sailing!)
Closed Christmas, Boxing & New Years Day
<u>Location:</u> On the main road through Cley

Norfolk: Heydon – Heydon Village Tea Room

The Street
Heydon
Norfolk NR11 6DA
Tel: 01263 587719

Access: 1 step in
Parking 10-25m
No smoking

Set within a tiny, peaceful and privately owned village this tea room is housed within the village shop overlooking the green. An idyllic place for tea where savouries, cream teas and many cakes are on offer.

Opening times: Tues, Weds & Fri 10am-4.30pm, Thurs 11am-4.30pm, Sun 1-4.30pm, Bank Hols 12-4.30pm.
Location: B1149 Holt road from Norwich

Norfolk: Holt – The Owl Tea Rooms

Janaway House, Church St
Holt
Norfolk NR25 6BB
Tel: 01263 713232

Access: 1 step in
Parking on street 20m
No smoking

Peering through the shop front window stacked with cakes and scones, it is hard to resist the urge to go inside this lovely tea room. Inside you will discover that all the food is home made, including the jams and chutneys. A popular place where you don't feel rushed.

Opening times: Mon-Sat 9am-5pm. Closed Bank Hols.
Location: Near the War Memorial in Holt

Norfolk: Norwich – Caley's Cocoa Café

The Guild Hall
Gaol Hill
Norwich NR2 1JP
Tel: 01603 629364

Access: flat throughout
Parking city centre
No smoking

Set in the historic Guild Hall in the heart of Norwich, the cocoa theme is evident throughout. Tablecloths are pristine white; there is good service and an excellent choice of cakes, of which Florentines are a speciality.

Opening times: Mon-Sat 8.30am-5pm. Closed Bank Holidays
Location: Near provisions market and City Hall

Norfolk: Norwich – King of Hearts Café

7-15 Fye Bridge Street
Norwich
Norfolk NR3 1LJ
Tel: 01603 620805

Access: full facilities to
ground floor
Parking: on street 30m
No smoking

This Tudor merchant's house with an attractive courtyard provides a delightful setting for tea and also houses a centre for arts where local artists exhibit their work. A really superb place that I look forward to returning to when I next visit Norwich.

Opening times: Mon-Sat 9am-5.15pm. Closed Bank Holidays
Location: Close to Cathedral & historic Elm Hill

84

Norfolk: Sheringham – Ye Olde Tea Rooms

7 Lifeboat Plain
Sheringham
Norfolk NR26 8BG
Tel: 01263 821532

Access: 1 low step in
2 within
Parking 10-25m
No smoking

The double bay fronted windows displaying traditional china beckon you into this delightful tea room in a very busy Norfolk town with many eating places. Do not miss this one for it is well worth a visit.

Opening times: April-Oct Tues-Sun 10.30am-5pm, Nov-March Thurs-Sun 11am-4pm
Location: Off main road behind Crown pub close to sea

Suffolk: Bury St Edmunds – Harriets Café Tearooms

57 Cornhill Buildings
Bury St Edmunds
Suffolk IP33 1BT
Tel: 01284 756256

Access: full facilities
Parking within 100m
No smoking

This traditional tea room is light and airy, with large windows to either end. There is an excellent range of quality loose leaf teas, with simply wonderful savouries, cakes and tea time treats. A marvellous place.

Opening times: Mon-Weds 9am-5.30pm, Thurs-Sat 9am-9pm, Sundays 10am-5.30pm
Location: Close to the market

Suffolk: Creeting St Mary –
Alder Carr Farm Tea Room

St Mary's Road
Creeting St Mary
Suffolk IP6 8LZ
Tel: 01449 720820

Access: full facilities
Parking on site
No smoking

With a good choice of delicious savouries and cakes, the emphasis at this tea room is on freshly prepared and locally sourced food, much of it from the farm shop. Look out for the Alder Carr ice cream.

Opening times: Tues-Sun 10.30am-4.30pm. Check for Winter closing. Closed 1st week Oct & 4 from 24 Dec
Location: Signs to farm off High St Needham Market

Suffolk: Debenham – Carters Teapot Pottery

Low Debenham
Suffolk P14 6QU
Tel: 01728 860475

Access: 1 step in
Parking outside
No smoking

This small tea room is set within Carters Teapot Pottery where fascinating, and useable, teapots are made and displayed. Tea may be served in any one of these; to be enjoyed with home made cakes or scones.

Opening times: Mon-Fri 9am-5.30pm, Sat & Bank Hols. 10.30am-4.30pm, Easter-Christmas Sun 2-5pm. Closed Christmas
Location: Brown tourist route signs from A14/A140

Suffolk: Lowestoft – Flying Fifteens

19a The Esplanade
Lowestoft
Suffolk NR33 0QG
Tel: 01502 581188

Access: flat to garden,
6 to tea room/toilet
Parking within 50m
No smoking

It is a wonderful surprise to find a proper tea room amid a host of seaside cafés and restaurants. Flying Fifteens offers friendly and efficient service, quality loose leaf teas. The wonderful scones are a speciality.

Opening times: Spring Bank Hol. to mid-Sept Tues-Sun & Bank Hols 10.30am-5pm. Easter Sat to Spring Bank Holiday weekends only. Closed mid-Sept to Easter
Location: Entrance via sea front, on South Beach near Hotel Hatfield

East Midlands

Derbyshire
Leicestershire
Lincolnshire
Northamptonshire
Nottinghamshire
Rutland

Derbyshire: Ashbourne – Bennetts

19-23 St John Street
Ashbourne
Derbyshire DE6 1GP
Tel: 01335 300394

Access: upstairs on
2nd floor
Parking town/Market
Place car park 50m
No smoking

Housed in a traditional, independent department store, the tea room is a haven from the bustle of the busy town. Relax over loose leaf tea and excellent food from breakfasts and lunches to afternoon teas. A real treat.

<u>Opening times:</u> Mon-Sat: 9am-4.15pm
<u>Location:</u> On the main shopping street in Ashbourne

Derbyshire: Bakewell – Byways Tea Room

Water Lane
Bakewell
Derbyshire DE45 1EU
Tel: 01629 812807

Access: upstairs
Parking: 50-100m
No smoking

In a small town with many tea rooms, Byways is definitely one not to miss. A traditional tea room complete with creaking, sloping floors and a fabulous menu including speciality Rarebits and loose leaf tea.

<u>Opening times:</u> Mon-Fri: 9am-4pm, Saturdays 9am-4.30pm, Sundays & Bank Hols. 9.30am-4.30pm
Closed Christmas Day, Boxing Day, New Years Day
<u>Location:</u> Centre of Bakewell

Derbyshire: Bakewell – Doddarelli's

Sinclairs, 1 The Square 🌿
Bakewell
Derbyshire DE45 1BT
Tel: 01629 813795

Access: upstairs
Parking: 50m
No smoking

On returning to this tea room, I was delighted to find the same high standards. There is great emphasis on home made, locally sourced food here, with splendid jams, scones, biscuits and savouries all made in house.

Opening times: Mon & Sat 9am-4pm, Tues-Fri 10am-4pm. Open Bank Hols. Closed Christmas/Boxing Day
Location: Centre of Bakewell above Sinclairs

Derbyshire: Chesterfield – Northern Tea Merchants

Crown House 🌿
193 Chatsworth Road
Chesterfield
Derbyshire S40 2BA
Tel: 01246 232600

Access: full facilities
Parking: on site/outside
No smoking

From humble beginnings as a simple tea bar, Northern Tea Merchants is now a 'proper tea room' with simple, delicious food, and an extensive tea menu. A place to relax whilst considering which of the many teas you might purchase to take home. Quite wonderful.

Opening times: Mon-Sat 9am-5pm. Closed Bank Hols.
Location: A619 from Chesterfield - Chatsworth House

Derbyshire: Derby –
Derby Cathedral Centre Coffee Shop

Derby Cathedral Centre
18/19 Iron Gate
Derby DE1 3GP
Tel: 01332 341201

Access: full facilities
Parking on street 25m
No smoking

It is no surprise that this coffee shop won the Derbyshire Food and Drink Award 2004 and was Highly Commended in 2005. The emphasis is on quality local, and fair trade food and drinks. A superb place.

Opening times: Mon-Sat 9.30am-4.30pm. Closed Bank Holidays
Location: Opposite Derby Cathedral

Derbyshire: Eyam – The Rookery

Main Road
Eyam, Hope Valley
Derbyshire
Tel: 01433 639666

Access: upstairs
Parking on site
Smoking in garden
area only

A tea room where you feel welcomed, as if to a friend's sitting room, with specialities like unique Plague Pie. You can sit outside on the patio or in the picture gallery red tea room surrounded by an array of paintings.

Opening times: Daily 10am-5pm. Closed Christmas, Boxing and New Year's Day
Location: Between Eyam Hall & Post Office

Leicestershire: Anstey – Broughton's Interiors

75 Cropston Road
Anstey
Leics LE7 7BP
Tel: 0116 2340700

Access: upstairs,
downstairs on request
Parking on site
No smoking

Enjoy excellent sandwiches and cakes in the stylish surroundings, which is part of Broughton's showroom with oak furniture and unique home accessories. A relaxed, calm atmosphere and a quality tea room.

Opening times: Mon-Sat 9.30am-4.30pm, Sun 10am-4pm. Closed bank Holidays
Location: From Anstey village take the Cropston road

Leicestershire: Market Bosworth – The Victorian Tea Parlour

The Wheatsheaf Courtyard
7 Market Place
Market Bosworth
Leics CV13 6NP
Tel: 01455 290190

Access: low step to
courtyard, flat within
Parking 10/25m
No smoking

It is a delight to sit in this traditional tea room with lace tablecloths, savouring good food. The home made cakes are quite delicious and very popular.

Opening times Tues-Sun & Bank Hols 10am–5pm. Closed Christmas Eve/ Day, Boxing Day
Location: Opposite the Square, to rear of Courtyard

Leicestershire: Rothley – Templars

5 Woodgate
Rothley
Leicestershire LE7 7LL
Tel: 0116 2302638

Access: 2 steps in, 2
within
Parking on street 20m
No smoking

Set to the rear of a gift shop, you can sit and relax over quality food in a pleasing and relaxing atmosphere whilst considering your purchases. A real find in an attractive Leicestershire village.

Opening times: Mon-Sat 10am-5pm. Closed Bank Hols. & Christmas/New Year
Location: On the main street in Rothley

Leicestershire: Staunton Harold – Staunton Stables Tea and Luncheon Rooms

The Ferrers Centre
Staunton Harold
Nr Ashby de la Zouch
Leics LE65 1RU

Access: full facilities
Parking on site
No smoking
Tel: 01332 864617

Although this tea room has expanded since my first visit many years ago, it has lost none of its charm or good quality. A great choice of cakes on offer in a tea room popular with the many visitors to the area.

Opening times: Tues-Sun & Bank Hols. 10am-5pm. Closed Christmas, Boxing, New Years Day
Location: Follow brown tourist signs to Ferrers Centre

Lincolnshire: Boston – Sack Store Café

Sack Store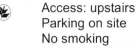
Spalding Road
Boston
Lincolnshire PE21 8EA

Access: upstairs
Parking on site
No smoking
Tel: 01205 310101

This tea room set in a former British Rail sack store, won Lincolnshire Life's Best Tea Room Award each year from 2002-2005. The menu has imaginative home made food, with choices for a variety of dietary needs.

<u>Opening times:</u> Mon-Sat 9am-5pm, Sun & Bank Hols. 11am-4pm. Closed 25/26/31 December & 1 January
<u>Location:</u> Follow brown tourist signs to The Sack Store

Lincolnshire: Caistor – Top House Tea Rooms

23 Grimsby Road
Caistor
Lincolnshire LN7 6RJ
Tel: 01472 859051

Access: full facilities
Parking on site
No smoking

Set in a Grade II listed building with awards for conservation, this tastefully restored, spacious tea room has a simple menu, table service and classical music. A family-run affair, this is a real peaceful haven.

<u>Opening times:</u> March-October Fri-Sun & Bank Holidays 11.30am-5.30pm. Closed Winter
<u>Location:</u> Midway between Market Rasen & the coast on A46 junction with A1173 at Caistor top

Lincolnshire: Fulbeck – Fulbeck Tea Rooms

Manor Stables Craft
Workshops, Fulbeck
Lincolnshire NG32 3JN
Tel: 01400 273724

Access: 1 low step in
toilet large/level
Parking on site
No smoking

A comfortable tea room serving loose leaf teas from
Imperial Tea in Lincoln, plus a splendid range of
savouries and teatime treats. The friendly proprietors
are kept busy with local children buying loose sweets.

Opening times: Tues-Sun & Bank Hols. 10.30am-
4.30pm. Closed 2 weeks at Christmas
Location: A607 between Lincoln and Grantham

Lincolnshire: Lincoln – Pimento Tearooms

26/27 Steep Hill
Lincoln LN2 1LU
Tel: 01522 544880

Access: upstairs
Parking: top of hill
No smoking

Set on several levels, Pimento is a wonderful tea room
with oak tables and a vast range of loose leaf teas from
the tea merchant, Imperial Tea, housed below. All food
is vegetarian or vegan, with vegan cakes on offer. It
really was a pleasure to return here.

Opening times: Mon-Sat 10am-5pm, Sun/Bank Hols.
10.30am-5pm. Closed Christmas, Boxing, New Years
Day
Location: Down the hill from Lincoln Cathedral

95

Lincolnshire: Louth – Chuzzlewits

26 Upgate
Louth
Lincolnshire LN11 9ET
Tel: 01507 611171

Access: 2 steps in, 1 within, 2 to toilet
Parking within 50m
No smoking

Chuzzlewits serves a good range of Taylors loose leaf teas including many of my favourites, such as Kwazulu. This is a popular, traditional tea room with set teas, excellent service from staff in black and white uniform.

Opening times: Weds-Sat 10am-5pm. Closed Bank Holidays
Location: 50m from church – look for 295ft spire

Lincolnshire: Stamford – Sam's Place

11-12 St Mary's Street
Stamford
Lincolnshire PE9 2DE
Tel: 01780 766511

Access: upstairs
Parking on street 50m
No smoking

A delightful tea room, where the scones are quite wonderful, set above Sinclair's china shop. The service is friendly and efficient, the food delicious; making Sam's Place a great place to relax and perhaps ponder a china purchase.

Opening times: Mon-Sat 9.30am-4pm. Closed Bank Holidays
Location: Up hill from the town bridge

Northamptonshire: Thrapston – Tasty Bite Victorian Tea Shoppe

34 High Street
Thrapston
Northants NN14 4JH
Tel: 01832 733070

Access: flat to enter,
1 step to some tables
Parking opposite
No smoking

Set in a listed building with large, shop front windows, this tea room evokes the Victorian era in its décor. A range of good, home made food is on offer.

Opening times: Mon-Fri: 10am-5pm. Sat: 9.30am-4.30pm. Closed Bank Hols & Christmas-New Year
Location: On main street in Thrapston

Northamptonshire: Weekley – Jessica's Tea Room

Weekley Post Office
Weekley
Northants NN16 9UN
Tel: 01536 482312

Access: flat, 2 steps to
conservatory 2 to toilet
Parking outside/25m
No smoking

Tea and delicious home made food can be enjoyed within this post office tea room or outside in the attractive garden. A superb selection of tempting cakes, with something for a range of dietary needs.

Opening times: Mon, Tues & Thurs-Sat 9am-4pm, Sun 11am-4pm. Closed 25/26 Dec/sometimes all week
Location: Look for thatched Post Office in village

Nottinghamshire: Bothamsall – Thaymar Tea Rooms

Houghton Park Farm
Nr Bothamsall
Nottinghamshire DN22 8DB
Tel: 01623 862632

Access: full facilities
Parking on site
No smoking

A truly traditional farmhouse tea room, with delicious home made cakes such as lemon or date and walnut. They also have over 40 different types of home made ice cream, which you can watch being made.

Opening times: 10am-5pm daily
Location: On B6387 ½ mile from A1 towards Bothamsall, Walesby & Ollerton

Nottinghamshire: Bulcote – Mulberries Coffee Shop

Tall Trees Garden Centre
Main Road, Bulcote
Nottinghamshire NG14 5GT
Tel: 0115 9312830

Access: full facilities
No smoking inside
Parking on site

It was a real surprise to find this tea room, within a garden centre, serving an incredible range of up to 150 different loose leaf teas and tisanes. A great place.

Opening times: Mon-Sat 9.30am-6pm, Sun 11am-5pm. Closed Christmas, Boxing and New Year's Day
Location: Between Burton Joyce & Lowdham on A612 Nottingham – Southwell Road.

Nottinghamshire: Newark - Old Bakery Tea Rooms

Queen's Head Court
Newark
Notts NG24 1EL
Tel: 01636 611501

Access: 1 low step in,
toilets/room 2 upstairs
No smoking
Parking within 50m

No self-respecting cake lover could possibly walk past this tea room, nor will they be disappointed. The proprietor is a cake maker par excellence and there are cakes for a variety of dietary needs.

Opening times: Tues-Sun 9.30am-5pm, open Bank Holidays but check first
Location: Close to the Market Square

Nottinghamshire: Sawley – Lock House Tea Room

Trent Lock
Lock Lane
Sawley Notts NG10 2FY
Tel: 0115 9722288

Access: flat throughout access. toilet at car pk.
Parking: Lock car park
No smoking

Set in the original lock house, this is a beautiful spot from which to observe canal life. With traditional fare and loose leaf teas, this is an experience to savour.

Opening times: Summer Weds-Sun 10am-6pm, Winter Weds-Sun 10am-4pm. Open Bank Hols, closed Christmas Day
Location: From airport head for Long Eaton & follow signs to lock

Rutland: Oakham – Flores Delicatessen

34b High Street Access: flat throughout
Oakham   Parking within 50m
Rutland LE15 6AL   No smoking
Tel: 01572 755601

Beamed ceilings, wooden floors, soft music, and newspapers to read characterise this tea room. I first tried Moroccan Mint Tea here and am now a great fan. The almond croissants are also divine. This is a place to relax; somewhere I hope to return to very soon.

Opening times: Mon-Sat & Bank Hols. 8.30am-5pm
Location: On main street through Oakham

Rutland: Uppingham – Baines Tea Room

1a High Street West Access: flat throughout
Uppingham   Parking within 50m
Rutland LE15 9QB   No smoking
Tel: 01572 822776

Housed within an old, oak-beamed building from which, at two large tables occupying the bay windows, you can watch the world go by whilst savouring excellent loose leaf teas and food. A traditional tea room for over 40 years, it is popular with locals and visitors alike.

Opening times: Mon-Sat 8.30am-5pm. Closed Bank Holidays & last week in December
Location: Close to Market Place in centre of the town

100

Yorkshire

North Yorkshire
West Yorkshire

North Yorkshire: Beckwithshaw – Bettys Café Tea Rooms

Royal Horticultural Society
Harlow Carr, Crag Lane
Beckwithshaw, Harrogate
North Yorkshire HG1 1QB

Access: full facilities
Parking on site
No smoking
Tel: 01423 505604

This tea room, the first new Bettys to open in 30 years, has an exquisite setting overlooking the gardens at Harlow Carr and is set within a beautiful room, where a pianist plays on Sundays. This is a wonderful experience and one most definitely not to be missed.

<u>Opening times:</u> Daily 9am-5.30pm
<u>Location:</u> Follow signs for RHS Harlow Carr

North Yorkshire: Clapham – Café Anne

Guildersbank
Clapham
North Yorkshire LA2 8EG
Tel: 01524 251716

Access: flat in & within
Parking: car park 15m
Smoking permitted by
the door

Still marvellously eccentric and still serving magnificent home made cakes – try the chocolate cake as you take in the vast number of art postcards and posters on every available wall and ceiling space.

<u>Opening times:</u> Weds-Sun & Bank Hols 10am-whenever! Generally closed weekdays in Winter
<u>Location:</u> Just beyond car park

102

North Yorkshire: Harrogate - Bettys Café Tea Rooms

1 Parliament Street
Harrogate
North Yorkshire HG1 2QU
Tel: 01423 877300

Access: downstairs
Parking on street
No smoking

On two floors, Bettys has been here since the 1930's and certainly stands the test of time. The glass fronted corner window is impressive, with its display of breads, cakes and chocolate. A memorable place for tea.

<u>Opening times:</u> Daily 9am-9pm.
<u>Location:</u> Opposite war memorial – centre of Harrogate

North Yorkshire: Helmsley – Vinehouse Café

Helmsley Walled Garden
Cleveland Way
Helmsley
North Yorkshire YO62 5AH
Tel: 01439 771427

Access: full facilities
Parking on site for
disabled people, or
nearby car park
Smoking outside only

A relaxed setting in a newly restored Victorian vine house, this tea room specialises in organic, fair trade and local produce - including items from the walled garden. Cakes are available for different dietary needs.

<u>Opening times:</u> Mon-Sat 10.30am-5pm. Closed Oct 31st–April 1st. Open Good Friday if it falls in March.
<u>Location:</u> Turn off by Feversham Arms

103

North Yorkshire: Ilkley – Bettys Café Tea Rooms

32 The Grove
Ilkley
North Yorkshire LS29 9EE
Tel: 01943 608029

Access: full facilities
Parking to rear
No smoking

Having been shown to your seat by welcoming staff, sit back and enjoy fine teas and speciality food, such as Fat Rascals, in a light, airy atmosphere. It is hard not to be captivated by the impressive display of teapots.

Opening times: Daily 9am-5.30pm
Location: Centre of Ilkley with car park to rear

North Yorkshire: Northallerton – Bettys Café Tea Rooms

High Street
Northallerton
North Yorkshire DL7 8LF
Tel: 01609 775154

Access: full facilities
Parking: car park 50m
No smoking

The elegant décor and furnishings create a soothing, calm atmosphere, and the domed glass roof in the Palm Room brings light to this delightful Bettys Tea Room. Excellent food, service and tea make this a marvellous place at any time of day.

Opening times: Mon-Sat 9am-5.30pm, Sun 10am-5.30pm.
Location: On the High Street – main shopping street

North Yorkshire: York – Bettys Café Tea Rooms

6-8 St Helen's Square
York YO1 2QP
Tel: 01904 659142

Access: full facilities
Parking: City car parks
No smoking

Opulent is the only way to describe this tea room at the heart of the city. There are huge windows with stained glass surrounds from which you can watch the hustle and bustle of York whilst indulging in excellent food and service, with loose leaf tea, of course. The Bettys experience at York is not one to be missed.

<u>Opening times:</u> Daily 9am-9pm
<u>Location:</u> Close to York Minster. The Park & Ride scheme will take you very near

North Yorkshire: York – Bullivant of York

15 Blake Street
York YO1 8QJ
Tel: 01904 671311

Access: 1 step in, 3 to
rear area + 1 to toilet
Parking: City car parks
No smoking

The window of Bullivant houses an impressive display of collectable teapots and inside the tables are set with pretty pink tablecloths in traditional style. A place to relax and indulge from the splendid menu.

<u>Opening times:</u> Mon-Fri 9.30am-5pm, Sat 9am-5pm, Sundays in Summer months only
<u>Location:</u> Close to York Minster

105

North Yorkshire: York – Little Bettys

46 Stonegate   Access: upstairs
York YO1 8AS   Parking: City car parks
Tel: 01904 622865   No smoking

This delightful little building has a shop on the ground floor selling Taylor's teas and coffees, with the tea room upstairs. Though small and intimate, it keeps to the excellent standards of all Bettys tea rooms – a lovely place for afternoon tea.

Opening times: Sun-Fri 10am-5.30pm, Sat 9am-5.30pm
Location: Close to York Minster, in pedestrianised area

West Yorkshire: Holmfirth – The Wrinkled Stocking

30 Huddersfield Road   Access: toilets upstairs
Holmfirth   Parking: car park 25m
West Yorkshire HD7 2JS   No smoking
Tel: 01484 681408

Take tea next door to Nora Batty's house where good quality, home made and healthy food is a speciality. The china used here is exclusive to The Wrinkled Stocking, adding to the 'Last of the Summer Wine' theme. A great welcome and a lovely tea room.

Opening times: Mon + Weds-Sun 10am-5pm, Bank Hols 11am-5pm. Closed Christmas & Boxing Day
Location: Next to Nora Batty's House!

West Yorkshire: Todmorden –
Exchange Coffee Company

Market Hall
Todmorden
West Yorkshire OL14 5AJ
Tel: 01706 839993

Access: flat
Parking outside market
Smoking permitted

This is my 'wild card' as you probably wouldn't consider a stand with high stools in a closed market to be a tea room. I was, however, charmed by its simplicity and commitment to loose leaf teas. Give it a go.

Opening times: Mon & Weds-Sat 9am-5pm, Tues 9am-1pm. Closed Bank Holidays
Location: Market Hall in centre of Todmorden

North West

Cheshire
Cumbria
Lancashire
Wirral

Cheshire: Dunham Massey –
Red House Farm Tea Room

Dunham Massey
Altrincham
Cheshire WA14 5RL
Tel: 0161 941 3480

Access: full facilities
Parking on site
No smoking

Part of a National Trust estate, this simple tea room offers a wonderful range of cakes, scones and savouries to enjoy with tea. The walls bear quotes about tea from famous people. Worth seeking out.

Opening times: Mon-Sat 9am-4pm, Sun & Bank Hols. 10am-3pm. Closed over Christmas/New Year
Location: Follow N.T. signs for Dunham Massey

Cheshire: Frodsham – The Cottage Tea Shop

121 Main Street
Frodsham
Cheshire WA6 7AF
Tel: 01928 733673

Access: 1 step in, 1 to toilet
Parking outside
No smoking

A delightfully traditional tea room in a building that was once a fish and chip shop. I heard a customer saying she came regularly for the fabulous cream teas. It was a pleasure to visit again, and thoroughly enjoyable.

Opening times: Tues, Weds, Fri 10am-4pm, Thurs & Sat 9.30am-4.30pm. Closed Bank Holidays
Location: Centre of Frodsham, on A56

Cheshire: Knutsford – Courtyard Coffee House

92 King Street (rear of)
Knutsford
Cheshire WA16 6ED
Tel: 01565 653974

Access: 1 step in, toilet
upstairs
Parking 25-50m

I remembered this tea room from my first visit and was delighted that it had not changed. It houses the Penny Farthing Museum and you may view the artefacts over tea and wonderful home made cakes or scones.

Opening times: Mon-Sat & Bank Hols. 9.30am-4.30pm. Closed Christmas & Boxing Day
Location: Rear of White Lion pub, up cobbled yard

Cheshire: Nantwich – Austin's Yesteryear Grocer and Coffee Shop

45 Hospital Street
Nantwich
Cheshire CW5 5RL
Tel: 01270 625491

Access: flat throughout
Parking: car park 25m
No smoking

The Coffee Shop is set around a fascinating museum style yesteryear grocer's shop, where walls are adorned with metal advertising signs. Enjoy the fine foods available in the actual shop of today.

Opening times: Tues-Sat 10am-3.30pm (early closing Weds). Closed Bank Holidays
Location: In Nantwich town centre close to square

Cheshire: Nantwich – Inglenook Tea Shoppe

42 Pillory Street
Nantwich
Cheshire CW5 5BG
Tel: 01270 610510

Access: low ridge in,
toilet with grabrails
Parking: car park 25m
No smoking

You are offered biscuits on arrival and sweets as you leave in this fun tea shop. They also serve Kwazulu tea, one of my personal favourites, and utterly delicious award-winning sticky tea bread.

Opening times: Mon-Sat 9.30am-4.30pm. Closed Bank Hols, except Good Friday
Location: Opposite museum, with car park at rear

Cheshire: Nantwich – Nantwich Bookshop Coffee Lounge

46 High Street
Nantwich
Cheshire CW5 5AS
Tel: 01270 619183

Access: upstairs
Parking: car parks
No smoking

Take a seat in leather armchairs in one of two rooms overlooking the High Street in this 16th century building above a bookshop. You can read the fascinating history from the menu while enjoying tea and cakes.

Opening times: Mon-Sat 9am-4.30pm. Closed Bank Holidays
Location: Pedestrianised zone, town centre square

Cumbria: Ambleside – Café Treff

4 Central Buildings
Ambleside
Cumbria LA22 9BS
Tel: 01539 431027

Access: 3 steps lower
room, toilet upstairs
Parking 50m
No smoking

Smart, chic, busy place with loose leaf tea served from cafetières. The menu states; "we looked hard for the best teacakes and think we found them". I agree, they were very fruity - a great accompaniment for your tea.

Opening times: Mon-Sat 10am-5pm. Closed Bank Holidays
Location: Opposite Market Cross shopping area

Cumbria: Appleby in Westmorland – Courtyard Gallery

32 Boroughgate
Appleby in Westmorland
Cumbria CA10 6XG
Tel: 01768 351638

Access: upstairs
Parking on street 25m
No smoking

This delightful gallery with a small tea room is set in a 350 year old building within a courtyard. Tea and delicious home made cakes are served using wonderful craft pottery. A very restful place indeed.

Opening times: Tues-Sun 10am-5pm. Closed Bank Hols. & Sundays from Christmas - Easter
Location: On main street on way up to castle

Cumbria: Bowness on Windermere –
Aunty Val's Tea Room

Church Street
Bowness on Windermere
Cumbria LA23 3DG
Tel: 01539 488211

Access: flat throughout
Parking 25m
No smoking

This traditional tea room where teapots hang from the beams is set in a busy lakeside town. A good range of loose leaf teas is available, along with savouries, cakes and scones all of which are served to your table.

Opening times: Daily 11am-5pm, closed Fri. in Winter
Location: Behind St Martin's church, near Steamer Pier

Cumbria: Carlisle – John Watt & Son Est. 1865

11 Bank Street
Carlisle CA3 8HG
Tel: 01228 521545

Access: on 2 levels
1st flat, 3 steps to 2nd
Parking: car parks
No smoking

Set within a tea and coffee merchant, you can smell the coffee beans roasting as you approach, so follow your nose. An excellent choice of loose leaf teas and the chance to buy more if you can't decide. Superb place.

Opening times: Mon-Sat 9am-4.30pm. Whit & August Bank Hols 10am-4pm. Closed other Bank Hols.
Location: Pedestrian area opposite Marks and Spencer

113

Cumbria: Culgaith – Mrs Millers Tea Room

Hazel Dene Nursery
Culgaith, Penrith
Cumbria CA10 1QF
Tel: 01768 88252

Access: full facilities
Parking outside or
car park 200m
No smoking

Mrs Millers is housed within a tastefully restored railway warehouse and has interesting memorabilia from the Settle to Carlisle railway. The restful atmosphere and excellent food make it a place you won't want to miss.

Opening times: Daily 9.30am-5pm. Closed Christmas Day, Boxing Day and New Year's Day
Location: Signposted from A66

Cumbria: Dent – Stone Close Tea Room

Main Street
Dent
Cumbria LA10 5QL
Tel: 01539 625231

Access: flat throughout
Parking: public car
park adjacent
No smoking

From marvellous, and satisfying set teas to Molly cake (dairy, egg, fat, sugar and gluten free *and* delicious), this tea room with oak beams and wooden pews has spectacular surroundings. Certainly worth the journey.

Opening times: Tues-Thurs 12-4.30pm, Sat & Sun 12-5pm. Open Bank Hols except 24, 25, 31 December
Location: Next to car park entrance (where there is an accessible toilet – key at tea room)

114

Cumbria: Garrigill – Thortergill Tea Rooms

Thortergill Forge
Garrigill, Alston
Cumbria CA9 3DH
Tel: 01434 381936

Access: 2 steps in,
toilet plus more tables
upstairs
Parking on site
No smoking

I was delighted to find this tea room still open as I had so much enjoyed my first visit. The setting is idyllic, the cakes divine, service friendly and teas are loose leaf. A must visit - well worth the spectacular drive.

Opening times: Tues-Sun 10am-5pm, incl. Bank Hols. Closed mid-November – early March
Location: Brown tourist signs from A686 or B6277

Cumbria: Hawkshead – Poppi Red

Main Street
Hawkshead
Cumbria LA22 0NT
Tel: 01539 436434

Access: 3 steps in
Parking: car park
No smoking

Poppi Red is worth a visit if only for the quirky and colourful teapots, cups and jugs. It also serves cakes which are very hard to resist, with local specialities such as Hawkshead tea bread with cheese.

Opening times: Summer daily 9am-6pm, Winter daily 9.30am-5pm. Closed 25/26 Dec & 1 January
Location: Centre of pedestrianised village

Cumbria: Kendal – Farrers

13 Stricklandgate
Kendal
Cumbria LA9 4LY
Tel: 01539 731707

Access: on 3 levels,
stairs to all levels
Parking 150m
No smoking

Farrers is set in a building on many levels dating back to 1649. Expect good loose leaf tea, simple fare and somewhere to relax over conversation or newspapers as you take in the historic atmosphere. Farrers has been a tea and coffee merchant since 1819.

<u>Opening times:</u> Mon-Sat 9am-5.30pm. Closed Bank Holidays
<u>Location:</u> in pedestrianised area of Kendal

Cumbria: Kendal – Tapestry Tearooms

Quaker Tapestry Exhibition
Centre, Stramongate
Kendal, Cumbria LA9 4BH
Tel: 01539 722975

Access: full facilities
Parking on site
No smoking

This little tea room serves good home made vegetarian fare in calm, relaxed surroundings. The staff are welcoming and friendly, and it is worth a visit whether or not you go to the fascinating tapestry exhibition.

<u>Opening times:</u> Mon-Fri 10am-4.30pm. Closed Bank Hols & Christmas – New Year
<u>Location:</u> Follow signs for Tapestry Exhibition

Cumbria: Kirkby Lonsdale – The Cariad Coffee House and Tea Room

7 Market Square
Kirkby Lonsdale
Cumbria LA6 2AN
Tel: 01524 273271

Access: 1 step in
Parking: in square
No smoking

Cariad has a comprehensive lunchtime menu, along with teatime treats and a selection of loose leaf teas. Set in a small town with a host of eating places, don't miss out on this little gem, which I thoroughly enjoyed.

Opening times: Mon-Sat & Bank Hols 9.30am-5pm, Sun 10am-5pm. Closed Christmas Day only
Location: on the Market Square

Cumbria: Langwathby – Brief Encounter Coffee Shop

The Old Station
Langwathby, Penrith
Cumbria CA10 1NB
Tel: 01768 881902

Access: full facilities
Parking on site
No smoking

This tea room has considerable charm and is a must for those who love the romance of steam railways. It was a thrill to visit again and enjoy the excellent fare.

Opening times: 1 March – 31 Oct daily 9am-5pm. Nov to last Sunday before Christmas 10am-4pm
Location: On A686 Penrith to Alston

Cumbria: Little Salkeld – The Watermill

Little Salkeld   Access: 1 step in
Penrith   + accessible toilet
Cumbria CA10 1NN   Parking on site
Tel: 01768 881523   No smoking

With breads, cakes and scones made from flour from
the mill and eggs from the free range hens, everything
here is incredibly fresh and quite delicious. Loose leaf
tea, good service and a peaceful setting by the water
add to the charm. Well worth seeking out.

Opening times: Daily 10.30am-5pm. Closed Christmas
Eve to start of February
Location: Off A686 from Penrith to Langwathby

Cumbria: Long Marton – Hidden Corner Tea Room

Park House   Access: flat to garden/
Long Marton, Appleby   toilet, 3 steps tea room
Cumbria CA16 6BY   Parking on site
Tel: 01768 361344   No smoking

Sit in the conservatory or garden, where there is open
countryside as far as you can see. Tea is served in
antique teapots and old bone china cups in this
unhurried atmosphere. Definitely worth seeking out.

Opening times: Sat, Sun & Bank Hols. 10am-4pm.
Closed Christmas Day & New Years Day
Location: Long Marton take Dufton road approx 3 miles

Cumbria: Melmerby – The Village Bakery

Melmerby, Penrith Access: full facilities
Cumbria CA10 1HE   Parking on site
Tel: 01768 881811   No smoking

For me, no visit to Cumbria is complete without going to The Village Bakery. Their longstanding commitment to quality organic food and catering for a range of dietary needs throughout the menu is most impressive.

Opening times: Mon-Sat 8.30am-5pm, Sun 9.30am-5pm. Dec/Jan Sun-Fri 9.30am-3.30pm, Sat 8.30am-5pm. Closed Christmas, Boxing & New Year's Day
Location: On top side of village green

Cumbria: Stainton – Greystone House Farm Shop and Tearoom

Stainton   Access: 2 tables
Penrith   + access. toilet on flat
Cumbria CA11 0EF   Parking on site
Tel 01768 866952   No smoking

While waiting to be served you can peruse the marvellous cakes on offer to enjoy with your tea. A relaxed setting in a converted barn with pine tables specialising in quality home grown, home made food.

Opening times: Daily 10am-5.30pm. Last orders 5pm. Closed Christmas Day
Location: Signed from M6 Junction 40

119

Lancashire: Blackburn - Exchange Coffee Company

13-15 Fleming Square
Blackburn
Lancashire BB2 2DG
Tel: 01254 54258

Access: 1 step within
Parking to side of
Victorian Arcade
No smoking

You are positively encouraged to take your time and relax over newspapers – no "coffee to go" here. There are 60 teas to choose from, food and service are of an excellent standard and somehow you just feel really welcome. A place definitely worth a visit.

<u>Opening times:</u> Mon-Sat 9am-5.30pm. Closed Bank holidays
<u>Location:</u> Middle of Victorian Arcade

Lancashire: Blackburn - Exchange Coffee Company

Market Avenue
Blackburn
Lancashire BB1 6HQ
Tel: 01254 680500

Access: flat throughout
Parking
No smoking

Another of Exchange Coffee Company's Cappuccino Bars set within a thriving indoor market. Not a traditional tea room setting but I hope you will share my delight at drinking loose leaf tea within a busy market.

<u>Opening times:</u> Mon-Sat 8.30am-5pm. Closed Bank Holidays
<u>Location:</u> Opposite main precinct building on Penny St

120

Lancashire: Blackburn – Rhubarb

Blackburn Visitors Centre
50-54 Church Street
Blackburn, Lancs BB1 5AS
Tel: 0125 453277

Access: full facilities
Parking outside
No smoking

A smart and chic establishment, maintaining the best of tea room values and atmosphere. Organics, local and fair trade produce are the mainstay; the food most attractively presented. Enjoyed by people of all ages.

Opening times: Mon-Weds 10am-6.30pm, Thurs/Fri 10am-8pm, Sat 10am-4pm
Location: Centre of Blackburn near cathedral

Lancashire: Clitheroe – Exchange Coffee Company

24 Wellgate
Clitheroe
Lancashire BB7 2DP
Tel: 01200 442270

Access: 1 lower room, 1 upper, toilet upstairs
Parking outside
No smoking

I really like this tea room, set on two floors, with its traditional wooden furniture and unhurried atmosphere. Staff are knowledgeable about the teas and coffees on offer; you can choose any sold in the shop – including award-winning large leaf English Breakfast tea.

Opening times: Mon-Sat 9am-5.30pm. Closed Bank holidays
Location: Off Castle Street

121

Lancashire: Lytham – The Coffee Bean

77 Clifton Street   Access: 1 step in
Lytham   access. toilet to rear
Lancashire FY8 5ER   Parking to rear
Tel: 01253 731581   Smoking outside only

To the rear of a tea and coffee seller, The Coffee Bean offers friendly service, a good range of cakes and savouries and a choice of loose leaf teas in a stylish setting. Not to be missed.

Opening times: Mon-Sat 9.30am-5pm, Sun 11.30am-5pm, Bank Hols 11-4.30pm. Closed 25/26 Dec & 1 Jan
Location: On main road in Lytham

Lancashire: Mawdesley – Roberts & Co

Cedar Farm, Back Lane   Access: full facilities
Mawdesley, Nr Ormskirk   Parking on site
Lancashire L40 3SY   No smoking
Tel: 01704 822433

You may need to rest upon one of the comfy sofas to ponder your choice of fifty loose leaf teas or forty coffees. I tried Young Hyson, a green tea, which was most refreshing. A working coffee roastery and definitely a tea lovers' dream

Opening times: Tues-Sun & Bank Hols. 10am-5pm
Location: Follow brown tourist signs to Cedar Farm Galleries from A5209

Lancashire: Silverdale – Wolfhouse Gallery

Lindeth Road
Silverdale
Lancashire LA5 0TX
Tel: 01524 701405

Access: full facilities
Parking on site
No smoking

Set in a light, airy room with additional seating outside, the café at the Wolfhouse Gallery offers an excellent range of cakes and savouries. A great place to consider a possible purchase from the gallery.

Opening times: Tues-Sun & Bank Hols. 10.30am-5pm. Closed in January
Location: Follow road through Silverdale to signs

Wirral: Heswall – Rose's Tea Room

23 Milner Road
Heswall
Wirral CH60 5RT
Tel: 0151 3429912

Access: flat in & within
1 small step to toilet
Parking outside

It was a surprise to come across such an elegant and tasteful tea room on an otherwise ordinary row of shops. Sardines on toast with loose leaf Kwazulu tea, made to perfection, was simply heaven. This tea room is simply too good to miss; go there.

Opening times: Mon-Sat 9am-5.30pm. Call to check for Bank Holiday opening
Location: Parallel Telegraph Rd, Heswall's main road

Northumbria

County Durham
Northumberland

County Durham: Barnard Castle –
The Market Place Tea Shop

29 Market Place
Barnard Castle
Durham DL12 8NE
Tel: 01833 690110

Access: on 2 levels
Parking outside
Smoking to rear only

I was delighted to find this tea room just as I remembered it from my last visit. A traditional tea room set in an attractive town, serving good home made fare.

Opening times: Mon-Sat 10am-5.30pm incl. Bank Holidays, Sun (March-Oct only) 2.30-5.30pm. Closed 2 weeks from 24th December
Location: Centre of town in cobbled Market Place

Northumberland: Blanchland –
The White Monk Tearoom

The Old School
Blanchland, Consett
Northumberland DH8 9ST
Tel: 01434 675044

Access: full facilities
Parking outside/30m
No smoking

With seating downstairs or on the mezzanine, this is a lovely tea room where there is good, traditional home baking from savouries to cakes and scones – superb.

Opening times: Easter to end Oct. daily 10.30am-5pm, weekends only November to Easter
Location: Centre of village

125

Northumberland: Falstone - Old School Tea Room

Falstone, Nr Kielder
Northumberland NE48 1AA
Tel: 01434 240459

Access: full facilities
Parking on site
No smoking

In 2004, this former village school was tastefully converted into an information centre, community shop and tea room, where environmental sustainability is a priority. A comfortable and friendly place for tea.

<u>Opening times:</u> Easter-Oct. daily 10.30am-4.30pm, Winter closed Tues & Weds and reduce hours to 11am-3pm. Closed Christmas Day
<u>Location:</u> Falstone off road from Bellingham - Kielder

Northumberland: Morpeth – Chantry Tea Room

9 Chantry Place
Morpeth
Northumberland NE61 1PJ
Tel: 01670 514414

Access: 1 step in
Parking on street or
town car parks
No smoking

Attracting locals from this busy small town, this is a quiet haven where good home made food and loose leaf teas are served at excellent value for money. This is a friendly place where It is easy to while away a peaceful hour or so.

<u>Opening times:</u> Mon-Sat 9am-4.30pm, incl. Bank Hols
<u>Location:</u> Off Newgate Street next to Chantry Bagpipe Museum

Northumberland: Simonburn –
Simonburn Village Shop and Tea Room

1 The Mains
Simonburn, Hexham
Northumberland NE48 3AW
Tel: 01434 681321

Access: 1 step in,
toilet with 1 handrail
Parking on site
No smoking

Excellent home made food, with vegetables and salads from the organic garden can be enjoyed indoors or outside in the pretty garden. This is a beautiful and peaceful setting; it's certainly hard to tear yourself away. Well worth seeking out.

Opening hours: Daily 9am-5pm. Closed Christmas Day
Location: Signed from A69 Hexham-Chollerford road

Index

129

131

133

Topsham (Devon) Georgian Tea Room   31
Totnes (Devon) Greys Dining Room   31
Trefin (Wales) Oriel-y-Felin Gallery and Tearoom   23

Uppingham (Rutland) Baines Tea Room   100

Walford (Herefordshire) Walford Court Garden   65
Warwick (Warwickshire) Brethren's Kitchen   70
Weekley (Northamptonshire) Jessica's Tea Rm.   97
West Mill (Hertfordshire) West Mill Tea Room   81
Winchelsea (E. Sussex) The Tea Tree   48
Windsor (Berkshire) Crooked House Tea Room   37
Woodstock (Oxfordshire) Hampers Food & Wine   41
Woodstock (Oxfordshire) Harriet's Tea Rooms   42

York (N. Yorkshire) Bettys Café Tea Rooms   105
York (N. Yorkshire) Bullivant of York   105
York (N. Yorkshire) Little Bettys   106

 Indicates loose leaf tea is served

135

Notes